Library of Congress Catalog Card Number: 61-10448

Printed in the United States of America

PLASTICS TOOLING

SECOND EDITION

MALCOLM W. RILEY
Associate Editor
Materials in Design Engineering

REINHOLD PUBLISHING CORPORATION, *NEW YORK*
CHAPMAN & HALL, LTD., *LONDON*

Preface

The success of plastics in any tooling program—even in one small tool—depends on understanding the plastics materials, and how they behave under various service conditions. The lack of such understanding will often lead to a misapplication of the material.

Basically it is a materials problem. Plastics, like metals, wood, and ceramics, comprise a family of engineering materials. In designing hard tooling the selection of the proper metal—whether cast iron, nodular or ductile iron, aluminum, "Kirksite," or steel—is based on (1) the engineering properties of the metal, which tell you how it will meet the physical and mechanical requirements of the tool, and (2) the methods by which the metal can be fabricated to the final required tool shape.

Plastics too offer (1) relatively well defined combinations of physical and mechanical properties (though not so clearly defined as those of metals), and (2) certain novel methods by which they can be put into a final tooling shape. Understanding these properties and fabrication methods permits an objective weighing of the materials versus other materials for a particular type of tool service. The purpose of this book is to provide the basis for such an understanding of tooling plastics.

The nature of plastics materials requires that the tool engineer know somewhat more about plastics chemistry than he need know about the metallurgy of tooling metals. Consequently, the discussions of the resins involve some of their chemistry. An attempt has been made to keep this to a minimum, and to provide only that type of information that will help both in working with the materials, and in working intelligently with plastics materials suppliers. Those interested in more chemical detail should consult the references at the ends of the chapters.

The term "plastics tooling" has come to connote those tools using plastics that can be cast, laminated or otherwise formed easily at relatively low temperatures to the final shape desired in the tool. Consequently, the only types of plastics tools *not* discussed here are those made from high-pressure laminates (industrial thermosetting laminates, e.g., "Formica" and "Micarta"). Although one of the first types of plastics used for tools, they primarily offer a standard sheet material of extremely high strength-to-weight ratio which can be machined to contour, usually by conventional woodworking techniques. Their major uses for the types of plastics tools discussed here are as structural support (e.g., egg-crate core constructions) or to form a level base.

The degree of commercial acceptance of a particular material or process should not be judged by the amount of space devoted to it in this book. Some of the materials and techniques described are quite new, e.g., metal fiber-reinforced epoxies. Some techniques are even developmental, e.g., gas or electroless nickel-plated surfaces for plastics tools. In each case I have tried to state clearly the degree of use. But I have also attempted to include as much data as possible to better describe those materials and techniques which appear to be highly promising in the future (as indicated by interest on the part of people working in the plastics tooling field).

The aircraft and auto industries have been the primary pioneers of plastics tooling—the aircraft industry because of (1) the relatively small volume of production parts, (2) need for speed, (3) use of relatively easily formed metals, such as aluminum, (4) preponderance of compound contours, and (5) in some cases the need for nonmetallic production tools in case of a shortage of metals.

The auto industry is highly cost- and time-conscious. First of all, much auto tooling is turned over to outside shops. Duplicate models and tools which can be simultaneously sent to several vendors and used by various production shops can substantially cut production lead time. Also, the degree of styling competition urges the development of lower-cost tools which permit more frequent modification of styling.

In the late '30's reinforced phenolic board was being widely used in aircraft tooling shops for small hand-forming blocks, as well as larger assembled fixtures. With the approach of World War II the aircraft industry became increasingly interested in plastics for tools because of the impending metal shortage. The greatest need, by both the aircraft and auto industries, was for a material that did not need machining to the final shape but could be formed directly to compound curvatures and complex shapes.

According to A. Juras, speaking to the ASTE, the first materials to meet these requirements in the late '30's and early '40's were the cast phenolics and ethyl cellulose. The phenolics used were relatively brittle, with high shrink; they required long cure times, and there were other problems. Ethyl cellulose, a thermoplastic, had to be melted and cast hot, and problems included high pour viscosity, excessive shrinkage, and internal strains in the final castings.

During the '40's polyester resins appeared on the scene—the first which could be successfully laminated with glass at low pressures. They were put to use in the aircraft industry for such tools as laminated jigs and fixtures. They overcame the brittleness of phenolics, and provided high strength and conformability. However, shrinkage was high, resulting in relatively poor dimensional accuracy and stability.

The '50's will probably be remembered as one of the major shake-down periods in plastics tooling. A status report on plastics tooling published in the form of a brief book in 1955 * indicated that at that time phenolics were still being used for many cast metal-forming tools. Polyesters were being pressure-cast for some metal-forming tools, and were still in use to a degree in jigs and fixtures. Ethyl cellulose was being used to provide resilience in drop hammer dies. Epoxies, which became prominent in tooling in early 1954, were showing their promise.

During the late '50's, epoxy resins fulfilled this promise. They could be laminated to provide toughness, overcoming the brittleness of phenolics in metal-forming dies. Improvements in both resins and formulations increased their heat resistance, which was the main point of argument for phenolics. Their extremely low shrinkage provided a high degree of dimensional accuracy, forcing polyesters out of the picture for those auxiliary tools requiring a high degree of accuracy. Finally, the development of resilient epoxy formulations appeared to solve, for the most part, the problems which still existed in the use of ethyl cellulose for such tools as drop hammer punches.

The result today is relatively clear. Epoxy resins dominate the plastics tooling picture. But, as mentioned before, other plastics materials can still be considered. Epoxies may be the best material for most plastics tooling uses, but other materials offer different combinations of engineering properties and costs. To most effectively use plastics as a tooling material, one must objectively evaluate all the materials and use the proper one in its proper place.

I have never made a plastics tool. My job is essentially technical reporting. Consequently the material for this book has been drawn from many sources. Particular thanks for a substantial amount of assistance are due Donald Soncrant of Modern Pattern and Plastics Co. who prepared Chapter 9 on Tool Design; A. Kerr of Union Carbide Plastics Co., Division of Union Carbide Corp., who reviewed Chapter 4 on Epoxy

* "Plastics Tooling," by Malcolm W. Riley, Reinhold Publishing Corporation.

Resins; L. F. Oye of Rezolin, Inc., who supplied much of the information for Chapter 2 on Organizing for Plastics Tooling; M. K. Young of United States Gypsum Co., for information on plaster mold making; and J. Delmonte of Furane Plastics, Inc.

A substantial amount of information has been drawn from papers presented at conferences of ASTME (American Society of Tool and Mfg. Engineers), SPI (The Society of The Plastics Industry, Inc.) and SPE, (Society of Plastics Engineers). Each of these societies has committees or groups specifically working on research, standards, and specifications for plastics tooling.

A particularly helpful summary of information is published in a booklet, "Plastic Tooling Symposium," sponsored jointly by the ASTME and SPI. Reference to specific papers published both here and elsewhere are given at the ends of the chapters.

Although a listing of helpful people and organizations cannot be complete, additional thanks are due personnel and literature of the following organizations:

Ciba Products Corp.; Coast Manufacturing and Supply Co.; Devcon Corp.; Dow Chemical Co.; Emerson & Cuming, Inc.; Fiber Metals, Inc., Subsidiary of Plastic Development and Research, Inc.; Ford Motor Co.; Furane Plastics, Inc.; General Electric Co., Silicone Products Dept.; Hexcel Products, Inc.; Marblette Corp.; Narmco Resins & Coatings Co.; National Cash Register Co.; National Institute of Management, Inc.; Owens-Corning Fiberglas Corp.; Ren Plastics, Inc.; Rezolin, Inc.; Shell Chemical Corp.; Smooth-On Mfg. Co.; Union Carbide Development Co., Div. of Union Carbide Corp.; Union Carbide Plastics Co., Div. of Union Carbide Corp.; United Merchants Industrial Fabrics, Div. of United Merchants & Manufacturers, Inc.

Finally, I would like to express my admiration for the ambidextrous agility of my wife, Barbara, who typed this manuscript while fielding three children.

MALCOLM W. RILEY

Centerport, N.Y.
February, 1961

Contents

1. *Why and Where to Use Plastics Tools*

A plastics tool is any tool made in whole or in part of a plastics material (excluding industrial thermosetting laminates, i.e., high-pressure laminates), and in which the plastic contributes substantially to the utility of the tool. Such tools range all the way from those made entirely of plastics to metal tools to which a plastics working surface has been applied.

There is only one proper approach to evaluating the suitability of plastics for a tool. That is to consider plastics as an independent family of engineering materials with unique (in the literal sense of the word) combinations of engineering properties, which indicate how the materials will behave under specific service conditions. Under some conditions plastics provide outstanding benefits in terms of lower cost, more rapidly fabricated tools, etc.; under other conditions, they should not be used at all.

The success of a particular plastics tool is solely dependent on the degree to which the tool engineer understands (1) the design requirements for the tool, and (2) the capabilities of plastics materials. The second area is the one causing most of the problems in plastics tooling today.

Linzell of Chrysler puts the problem succinctly: "Picture if you will, a die engineer specifying a material for a particular die detail. He knows exactly where he stands with iron and steel. He has ready material on hand that gives him weights, characteristics and costs. He also has his experience which tells him what to expect from a particular metal. On the other hand, he knows very little about plastics as a die material. Naturally he will specify that with which he is most familiar."

Becoming "familiar" with plastics is relatively simple; understanding them to the degree that their full capabilities can be realized is more difficult. Each member of the growing plastics family offers a relatively broad range of properties; but within each group, specific types offer more specific combinations of properties. In using metals, a standard alloy can be specified which is supplied within guaranteed compositional limits and often with guaranteed minimum strengths. In specifying and using plastics, no such standard grades exist. Also, for the most part, tooling plastics are "made" *in situ;* that is, the resin is catalyzed and cured in the tooling shop in the final shape of the tool. Since the way in which the material is formulated, catalyzed, fabricated and cured determines to a large degree the end-properties of the material, the tool engineer must have a greater understanding of the technology of plastics than he does of metals. The tool engineer unfamiliar with plastics should work closely with the materials supplier at the start. Reliable, reproducible physical properties can be obtained in plastics, but only by processing the materials properly.

Epoxies are the most widely used tooling plastics. They provide an excellent balance of physical and mechanical properties, low shrinkage, and compatibility with glass fiber reinforcements. A substantial portion of this book is devoted to these materials.

Other plastics should not be overlooked. Many of them can provide distinct advantages in tooling, if properly used. Phenolics provide high heat resistance; polyesters provide low materials cost and excellent processibility; room temperature-vulcanizing silicone rubbers (not actually a plastic) provide heat-resistant, flexible mold materials; foams of phenolic, epoxy and urethane provide high bulk with low weight; and so on. Such specialty applications as the use of flexible polyvinyl chloride for molds for concrete, nylon mandrels for machine- and hand-bending of aluminum tubing, and thermoformed thermoplastic sheet for molds for forming urethane foams indicate that other plastics also can offer benefits.

Advantages of Plastics for Tools

The primary benefits obtained by using plastics for tooling derive from the ability of these materials to reproduce contours and dimensions. Most tooling plastics are liquid thermosetting resins which are formed by casting or laminating directly against a plaster splash, a wooden or plastic master, or a prototype part, at room temperature. They can then be cured either at room temperature or with heat. These fabrication characteristics plus the properties of tooling plastics usually provide the following benefits in tooling:

Lower Cost Tools. With the proper resin and fabrication techniques the contour of the working face of the tool can be reproduced so accurately that no further machining or finishing is required. This ease of reproduction almost invariably results in lower tool costs.

For example, a die for stamping station wagon roof panels would cost about $38,000 in steel; in plastics the die was built for $22,000. An aircraft stretch die in Kirksite cost $256; in plastics the same die cost $152. An aluminum aircraft checking fixture cost $854; in plastics the fixture cost $330. A set of 12 auto fixtures in metal cost $68,000; in plastics they cost $33,000.

Degree of cost reduction varies with the tool. Estimates put average cost of plastics tools at 30 to 70 per cent less than the same tooling in

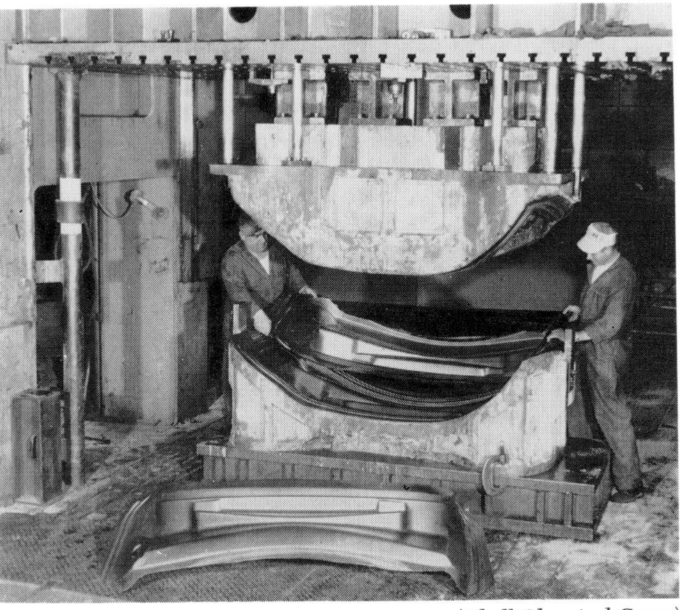

(*Shell Chemical Corp.*)

Figure 1.1. Draw dies such as this one, made by Allite Div. of Allied Products Corp., uses an epoxy-glass laminate surface over a cast metal core, and a lower pad of die iron, Kirksite or aluminum. Plastics faced punch costs about 30-60 per cent less than metal.

metal. In some cases, plastics tools may cost more than comparable metal tools, but other benefits such as light weight, may outweigh initial higher costs.

Plastics are almost invariably more expensive than metals. Epoxy resins, the most expensive of the tooling plastics, cost about 65 to 70¢/lb in large quantities, not including the cost of compounding ingredients, such as fillers, hardeners or curing agents. But materials costs are estimated to be only about 8 to 15 per cent of the total cost of a tool. Also, plastics have much lower densities than metals, ranging from 0.038 lb/cu in. for an unfilled cast phenolic to 0.064 lb/cu in. for a glass-reinforced epoxy laminate. Density of tooling metals ranges from a low of 0.097 lb/cu in. for aluminum, 0.239 lb/cu in. for cast zinc alloy, to 0.275 lb/cu in. for carbon and low-alloy steels. Consequently each pound of cast phenolic contains about 26.3 cu in. of material, and each pound of reinforced epoxy contains about 15.6 cu in. of material. Each pound of aluminum contains about 10.3 cu in., each pound of zinc alloy contains about 4.2 cu in., and each

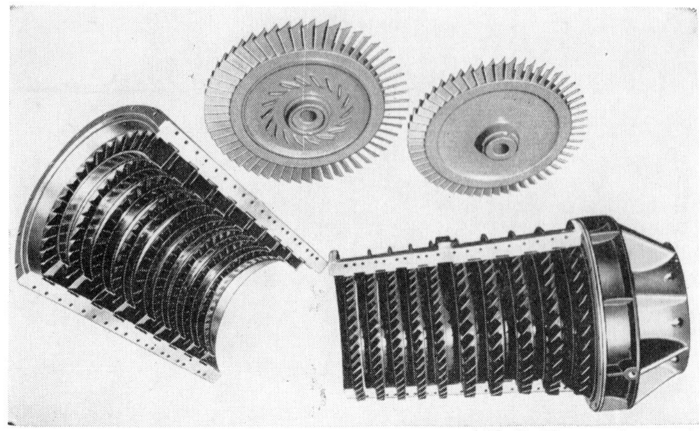

(*Shell Chemical Corp.*)

Figure 1.2. Demonstration model of Solar Aircraft's T-300 jet engine was accurately cast in epoxy resin by C. H. Miller Co. at 7 per cent of the estimated cost for metal. Model runs at 200 rpm, consequently tolerances of ±0.002 in. on rotor and almost zero on blades were critical.

pound of steel about 3.6 cu in. The lower density of plastics does lower the volumetric materials cost substantially.

Faster Tool Fabrication. Reductions in tool lead time obtained with plastics tools are usually caused by elimination of finishing operations. This is particularly true in the case of matched two-member tooling where the "bluing" or matching of the tool faces can be such a painstaking, time-consuming job (usually being done by highly paid die makers). Since the plastics are liquid at room temperature, tools can be duplicated rapidly by casting or laminating directly against a wooden model, or against the first tool produced from a model, or against a prototype or production part.

Where the tool is too large for effective heat-cure, or heat-curing facilities are not available, epoxy or polyester tools can be room-temperature cured. Cure cycles at room temperature are substantially longer than those at elevated temperatures. Consequently actual reduction in tool fabrication time is highly dependent on type of tool, and type of material of which it is made.

In many cases, tool production time can be reduced from months to weeks, or weeks to days. For example, the set of 12 auto fixtures mentioned above required 22 weeks lead time in metals; in plastics they

(*Furane Plastics Inc.*)

Figure 1.3. Large stretch die would be so heavy that it would be almost unmanageable in metal. Construction selected by Lockheed was cast epoxy face-backed with hollow aluminum core.

were delivered in 7 weeks. An experimental die for an advanced auto luggage compartment cover panel required 6 weeks to fabricate in plastics, compared to 8 to 10 weeks in Kirksite, or at least 12 weeks in cast iron.

Lighter Weight Tools. Weight reduction may or may not be a substantial advantage. In such tools as drill jigs, fixtures and other auxiliary tools which must be handled frequently during production, lighter weight is obviously beneficial in reducing worker fatigue and in speeding produc-

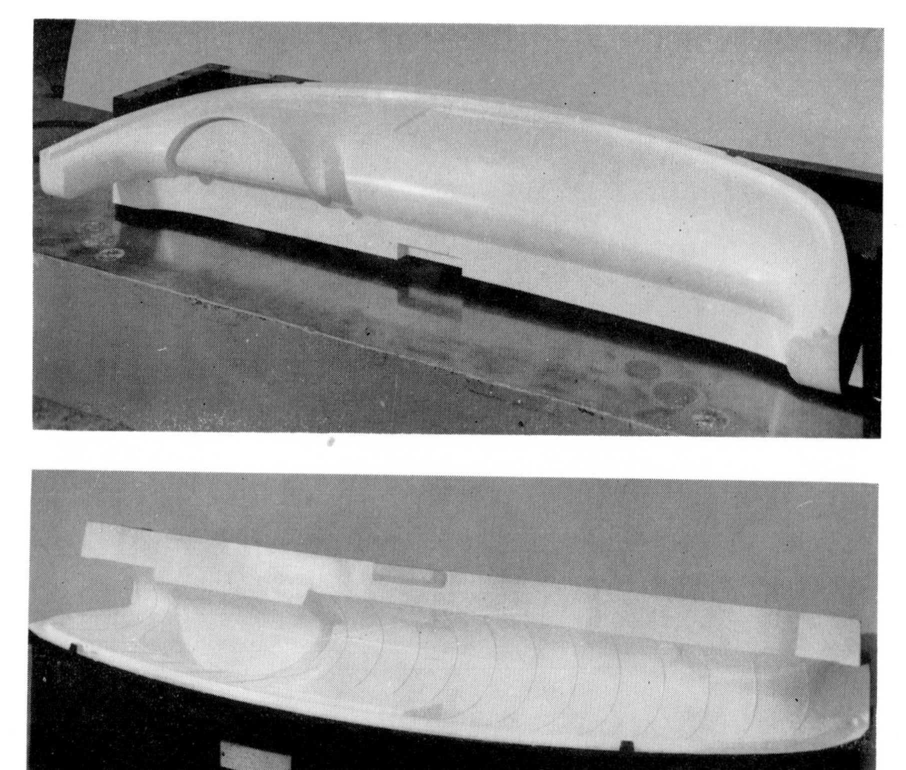

(*Ford Motor Co.*)

Figure 1.4. Complete male and female crash pad molds are supplied by Ford to their vendors, permitting Ford Engineering to retain responsibility for accuracy of the master mold. (*O'Reilly and Wyatt*)

tion operations. In large dies and fixtures moved infrequently, weight reduction may not be particularly desired, and often such tools require the additional stability provided by heavy weldments, or aggregate type cores. Also, weight may be required in some types of metal-forming dies.

Ease of Repair or Revision. The ease of machining of plastics, coupled with their liquid nature and excellent adhesive qualities make repair or revision of tools a relatively simple operation. Where the working surface of a plastics tool is either worn or ruptured, or where it requires alteration due to a modification of design, the face can be chipped out with a hammer and chisel, and the repair or modification made by a simple patching operation. Liquid patching resins adhere well to both the base metal or cured resin. The ease of revision is particularly useful in modifying and studying prototype designs.

Other Benefits. Certain of the tooling plastics have low moisture absorption, and excellent dimensional stability. Though this stability is not as good as that of metals, it is better than wood. Consequently plastics can be excellent replacements for wood for master models and duplicate die models.

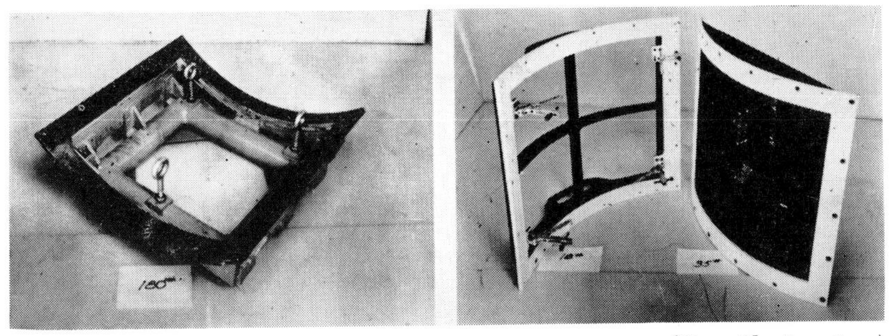

(*Ren Plastics, Inc.*)

Figure 1.5. Improvements in drill fixtures by use of plastics is shown by comparing the old 180-lb steel drill fixture at left with the 35-lb plastic fixture at right. In this case use of plastics permitted development of a trim fixture for use with the drill fixture. Cost of the two plastics fixtures was about 50 per cent that of the single steel fixture.

Chemical resistance of plastics can contribute substantially to longer tool life where tools must be stored and used intermittently. It is also important where tools must be used in contact with oils and greases.

Limitations of Plastics

The three most important limitations of plastics, as compared with metals, for tools are: (1) lower strengths, (2) lower heat resistance, and (3) the requirement for an accurate mold. Limitations as applied to each type of tooling are discussed in more detail in chapters discussing specific tooling applications.

Mechanical Strength. On a strength *per unit weight* basis some plastics —more specifically reinforced plastics—may be stronger than some metals. But on the basis of strength *per unit area* alone, plastics do not offer the ultimate mechanical strengths obtainable in metals.

Specific properties are compared in detail in Chapter 3. In general, tensile strengths of reinforced plastics are primarily dependent on orientation of the reinforcing fiber. Although tensile strengths as high as about 140,000-200,000 psi are obtainable in certain types of unidirectionally reinforced plastics, laminates used for tooling usually use fabric reinforcements which are essentially bidirectional (such as satin weave 181 or 1000 style fabrics). Consequently, tensile strength values of about

(*Ford Motor Co.*)

Figure 1.6. Plastics master spotting buck, believed by Ford to be one of the most complete ones ever built, incorporates most body structural and skin items except the roof. It includes openings for deck lid, windshield, back light, hood and door. (*O'Reilly and Wyatt*)

25,000 to 50,000 psi are more common. Also the effects of processing variables and such environmental factors as moisture usually require the use of lower values for design.

Heat Resistance. Resistance of tooling plastics to heat is generally of a different—and lower—order of magnitude than that of metals. The maximum use temperature of a material, of course, is dependent on time of exposure, and type and magnitude of stress imposed on the material. A material's strength decreases with increasing temperature and/or increasing time at temperature. Consequently, a maximum use temperature cannot be stated specifically. However, tooling plastics in general have been limited to maximum temperatures of about 200 to 250°F for lengthy exposure.

Some of the newer epoxy resins promise substantial improvements in heat resistance, with good strength retention in the 500°F temperature range. But practical factors such as processibility and cost have not been fully evaluated from the tooling standpoint.

The extremely low thermal conductivity of plastics is also undesirable in that (1) it insulates "hot spot" areas, contributing to heat build-up, possibly to the point of degradation of the plastic, and (2) it makes heating and the even distribution of heat over plastics-forming molds extremely difficult.

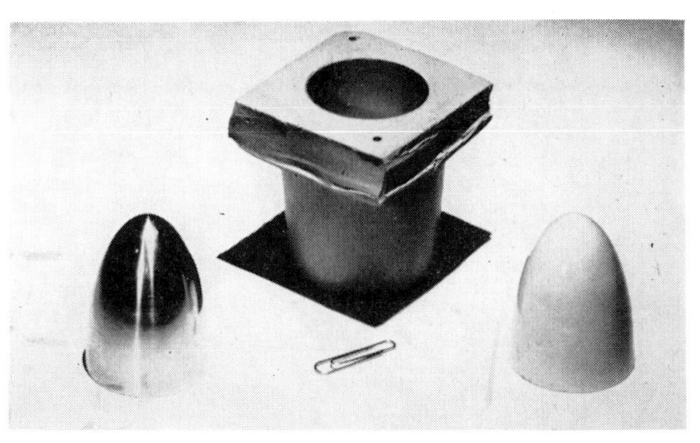

(*General Electric Co.*)

Figure 1.7. Flexible mold made of RTV (room temperature vulcanizing) silicone rubber (at center) provides cast epoxy nose cone (at right) with same high polish as that on the original aluminum model at left. No parting agent is required; this mold was used for 11 other nose cones.

Accurate Mold Required. One of the most important benefits of plastics for tools is the fact that the material can be formed directly into the desired finished shape. Consequently, plastics require an accurate mold. A plastics tool is only as accurate as the mold or master against which it is formed. In some cases, the expense and time required to fabricate an accurate mold for plastics may be as high as that required to machine and finish a metal tool. In such cases, the other benefits of plastics tools must be examined to determine whether or not a plastic tool will be advantageous. A factor which can weigh heavily in favor of plastics is that once an accurate mold or master is produced, it can usually be used to produce a number of plastics tools.

Hazards. There are some dangers in handling some types of plastics materials. For example, some types of amine hardeners for epoxies may be toxic, causing dermatitis; phenolics are cured with acid catalysts which must be handled with care; peroxide catalysts for polyesters may be explosive under certain conditions. However, using the proper precautions as recommended by plastics materials suppliers, plastics can be processed and handled without extraordinary hazards.

(*Marblette Corp.*)

Figure 1.8. Drop hammer punch made of cast epoxy over a metal core, forms relatively severe radii. This die lasted for more than 250 blows; similar lead dies required repair after 75 strikes.

Where Plastics Tools Are Used

The benefits of plastics tooling are available to virtually all phases of hard-good manufacture, ranging from initial product design to final assembly.

Product and Tool Design. In the initial design phases of any product, as well as in major design revisions, a three-dimensional model is produced to give the designer a better idea of how his design will look and work as an actual product. Traditionally such models have been made in clay or wood which can be reworked or modified relatively easily.

(*General Electric Co.*)

Figure 1.9. High temperature epoxy cast transistor fixture is oven-cured right in this flexible RTV silicone rubber mold.

When the model is finalized or approved, a "hard model" is usually made in wood or metal to serve as the production model.

A plastics model, produced by forming directly against the clay or wood, is low in cost. Also, a number of duplicate models can be made in plastics rapidly and economically. The immediate availability of a number of accurate duplicates can substantially reduce production time in that various departments, such as tool planning and production planning, can have exact models of the design virtually simultaneously. Also, sections of the product, such as quarter panels for cars, can be reproduced rapidly for fabrication and welding feasibility studies.

This economical reproducibility of masters and models can be of particular benefit when parts are to be supplied by outside fabricators or vendors. Instead of having only working drawings, vendors may now be supplied with accurate models of the part they are to produce.

The same economics available in plastics design models and masters is available in tooling masters and models, such as masters and duplicate masters for Keller and pantograph models or patterns; injection molding dies; matched metal draw dies; restrike dies; and other metal tooling.

(*Devcon Corp.*)

Figure 1.10. All-plastic punch and hold down ring, as well as mating die member used for drawing parabolic reflector were made by Amesbury Metal Co. by casting steel powder-filled epoxy.

Plastic master tooling can be so economical that complete sets of tooling masters can be supplied to vendors. For example, Ford had been supplying partial tooling to a vendor who was fabricating vinyl-covered urethane foam auto crash pads. The tooling supplied was limited to male "outside of metal" molds and male "outside of vinyl molds." The vendor then had to worry about "marrying" the two together. By supplying complete male and female plastics molds, Ford's engineering department could maintain control and responsibility for the accuracy of the master mold.

A relatively new development in the use of plastics tooling in original design is the use of plastics models for stress analysis. A model is cast in epoxy resin, cured and heated to the critical temperature. The part is then stressed as it will be in service, and cooled under stress. Resulting strains are thus locked into the part. Slices of the part are then taken from certain points, such as planes of symmetry or known principal planes, and stresses are computed by use of polarized light.

(*Kish Industries, Inc.; Shell Chemical Corp.*)

Figure 1.11. Cope and drag patterns for the oil pan of a diesel are made with an epoxy surface at International Harvester. Patterns are cheaper and faster to make, and provide improved sand release qualities.

Sheet Forming. Plastics tools are being used for both metal and plastics sheet forming, for low-to-medium production volume.

In sheet-metal forming, plastics matched draw and restrike, stretch-forming, and drop hammer dies, Hydroform and Hydropress punches, and blanking and trimming dies are being used successfully for short- and medium-run production. The resulting reduction in tool cost and lead time reduces quantity requirements for tool amortization and permits economical production of a smaller quantity of parts.

Plastics molds have also been used for explosive forming of metal. Although forming pressures are high, duration of load is extremely short. This is a relatively new forming method, and the value of plastics molds is far from firmly established.

Plastics molds are being successfully used for forming both reinforced plastics laminates and thermoplastic sheet. The lighter weight of plastics tools can be of particular benefit in plastics fabrication shops where heavy tool handling equipment may not be available. Also, some plastics shops may not have metal tool-making facilities, but have sufficient facilities to fabricate plastic tools.

Plastics molds are being used most widely for plastics forming operations requiring only moderate pressures and heat. They are commonly used for contact, bag and spray molding of reinforced plastics. They are also being used for vacuum or pressure forming of thermoplastic sheet. Where maximum production life is required such molds are water-cooled.

Fabrication and Assembly. One of the oldest and most firmly established uses for tooling plastics is for tools used as production, assembly and inspection aids. Such tools provide reference locations for assembly or manufacturing operations, or are used to inspect manufactured or assembled products during or after completion of the production operation. Such tools include checking fixtures, routing blocks, spotting racks, master gages and contour and trim line checking fixtures.

In addition to low cost and speed of fabrication, light weight is one of the most important attributes of plastics for such tools, as they are usually moved and handled frequently by production personnel. Such tools are not usually stressed heavily in use, and the critical requirements are accuracy, dimensional stability, and sufficient durability to withstand shop handling.

In the electrical and electronic industries, a relatively new development is the use of integral molds for potting or encapsulation of electrical assemblies. The term "integral molds" is used here to describe those molds which become integral parts of the finished assembly.

Component cases of the size required to contain the assembly, and usually made of the same material as the potting compound, are either fabricated or purchased. The components are located within the case serving as the mold. When the potting compound is cured, the assembly is complete, the mold serving as the outer surface of the completely encapsulated assembly.

Metal Foundry. Metal foundries are using plastics cope and drag plates, pattern plates and core boxes. Low cost, rapid production and reproduction, accuracy of detail, excellent parting qualities from sand molds, as well as light weight, are the primary benefits of such tools. In many cases, resilient plastics provide a high degree of abrasion resistance where accurate dimensions or good surface finish must be maintained.

Stonework. An interesting, off-beat development is the use of plastics molds to duplicate economically hand-carved stonework in concrete. Vinyl plastisol molds are cast to duplicate the stonework. Concrete is then poured into the molds, reproducing the detail precisely. For large parts, the vinyl mold is backed with casting plaster to provide the desired rigidity.

REFERENCES

1. Linzell, L. L., "A User Looks at Plastic Tooling," paper presented before the 16th Annual Conference, Reinforced Plastics Division, The Society of The Plastics Industry, Inc., Feb. 1960.
2. Godard, B. E., "Plastic Tooling, A Report on Present Progress," paper presented at Summer Meeting, Society of Automotive Engineers, June 1960.
3. O'Reilly, J. T. and Wyatt, H. L., "Our Experience in the Use of Plastics for Making of Duplicate Die Models, Engineering Checking Fixtures and Prototype Tools," paper presented before the 26th Annual Meeting, American Society of Tool Engineers, May 1958.

Note: The American Society of Tool Engineers (ASTE) has recently changed its name to American Society of Tool & Manufacturing Engineers (ASTME).

2. *Organizing for Plastics Tooling*

At some point while considering plastics tooling a decision must be made as to how deeply to get involved. Whether to organize your own plastics tooling design and fabrication shop or to farm work out to one of the competent job shops now in operation is a decision which can only be based on a careful and complete analysis of individual tooling needs. The decision depends on many factors, and will differ with each facility. The discussion here is intended only to indicate some of the more important factors to be considered, and give an idea of what is involved in setting up a shop. These factors should be kept in mind while considering specific materials and fabrication techniques.

Essentially, the feasibility of setting up a plastics tooling facility depends on (1) the volume and complexity of tooling work to be done, (2) the experience of available personnel, and (3) geographic location.

1. *Volume and Complexity.* The tooling volume must be such that the initial capital investment in setting up the shop as well as the overhead involved in operation are offset by the resulting reduction in tool cost.

An approach used effectively by many shops is to produce their own simple tools such as locating fixtures or jigs, but farm out complex, critical tooling jobs, such as draw dies.

2. *Experienced Personnel.* Shops with no experience in plastics tooling should usually have their first tools made by an experienced outside job shop. Gradually, the more simple tools can be produced in-plant, if experience indicates that such operations would be economical. Of course, plants in the plastics fabricating business have the benefit of people who know the materials. In such cases, they should carefully evaluate the problems peculiar to plastics tool design to determine whether they ought to produce such tools themselves initially.

3. *Locality.* The geographic location of the plant will have an important effect on the choice. Unfortunately today there are relatively few areas which have sufficient qualified plastics tooling job shops. In Detroit, there are more than one hundred such shops, many of which are

specialized in particular phases of plastics tooling work. But many other sections of the country are not so fortunate. In some cases, the decision to do-it-yourself may be made by the lack of qualified job shops to do tooling work.

Personnel

Objective, thinking supervision is probably the most important requirement of a good plastics tooling shop. Objectivity is essential in determining whether a tool should be made in plastic in the first place. Thought and imagination are essential in organizing and effectively fabricating the tool most economically. There are several ways of fabricating plastics; the proper method for a given tool provides the maximum benefits. Supervisory personnel should have experience in plastics fabrication, as well as hard tooling experience if possible. Once these requirements are met in supervision, the rest of the shop staff can usually be built around this nucleus quite easily.

Where is such a supervisory nucleus obtained? In setting up a captive shop it can often be found within the existing company. Often personnel in other departments on a lesser staff level are interested in the obvious opportunities of a new technology. Such people might be found in model-making departments, steel fabricating groups, or hard die groups. Pattern and model makers can be particularly useful because of their knowledge of blueprints and their training in making build-ups of wood. These people, trained by a few highly qualified plastics engineers, can form the core of a highly effective plastics tooling department.

Fabricating personnel could be drawn from among cabinetmakers, carpenters and others holding lesser positions in pattern-making and model-making departments. These people would have to be trained in plastics fabrication. The bulk of such training would be available from the plastics engineers in the supervisory group. Also, both the basic plastics materials suppliers and formulators usually have competent staffs of technical service engineers equipped to educate and assist customers—and potential customers—in the proper use of their materials. Several formulators have their own tooling shops for training newcomers to plastics tooling in proper engineering and fabrication techniques.

Facilities and Organization

The following discussion outlines facilities and organization usually required for a complete self-contained plastics tooling shop according to

L. J. Oye of Rezolin. In setting up a captive shop other departments already established within the company may be drawn upon to perform several functions such as template shops, and plaster model shops. Often, self-contained units provide maximum efficiency, but this will be highly dependent on individual situations.

Cost of facilities for plastic tool fabrication is lower than that for comparable metal tool fabrication. Of course, the size and type of plastic tools to be made have a direct bearing on the facilities required.

The building requirements are determined by climatic conditions and the project contemplated. But, in addition to floor space, adequate ventilation, lighting and head room should be provided. Sanitary facilities must also be available to all personnel who come in contact with uncured plastic materials. Showers and private clothing lockers, together with supervised personal hygiene, are highly desirable.

Like any other production department, a plastics tool-making shop should be organized for most efficient work flow, materials availability, and centralization of similar types of operations. The latter permits personnel to become specialists in particular operations.

In setting up the shop, small-scale production should be planned first, fabricating simple tools such as a holding fixture, contour checking fixture, simple vacuum forming mold, or small metal-forming die. With experience, such a shop can slowly grow into a complete shop to meet all your plastics tooling needs.

The complete shop should generally have the following sections: template, patterns and molds, welding and metal fabrication, mold preparation, plastics casting, plastics laminating, tool finishing, tool proofing, and service facilities.

Template. In most cases, templates are the source of dimensional control for molds and mock-ups used in the manufacture of plastics tools. They are generally of flat sheet metal—steel, aluminum or brass—and vary from 0.020 to 0.125 in. in thickness.

Facilities required to lay out and manufacture templates include lay-out tables, square shears, metal cutting band saws, band filers, drill presses and miscellaneous bench equipment for sheet metal work. Usually such a shop would include (1) the lay-out group: well-qualified "Class A" template makers who can read tool design and part drawings and carry out the calculations required to lay out accurate templates from engineering data supplied, and (2) template filers: lesser experienced personnel who can be readily trained.

Patterns and Molds. This is primarily a plaster pattern shop supplemented by a limited amount of woodworking equipment. The size and amount of equipment required will be determined by the size and type of tools to be produced. Requirements are generally similar for all small and medium-size tooling, such as duplicating models, foundry patterns, check fixtures, and small assembly tooling, i.e., small tooling that can be constructed on the average work table or surface plate. Additional equipment is required for larger tooling programs, such as encountered in the aircraft and automotive industries. Requirements usually include:

1. Set-up tables of surface plate quality. The working top may be of steel, plastic, cast iron, marble, or granite, machined and scraped or ground flat to tolerances of ± 0.002 in.

For larger tooling programs, surface plates would have to be large enough to handle the larger tools. If possible, such plates should be equipped with accessories needed to convert them into tooling docks. Also, for larger tools optical measuring equipment may be needed. Such equipment would consist of conventional surveyors' "Y" levels, transits, and if high precision work is contemplated, instruments such as colimeters, especially developed for tool checking.

2. Facilities for mixing and handling plaster. Manufacturers literature and technical bulletins provide additional information.

3. Basic woodworking equipment, including bench saw with tilting arbor, band saw, disk sander, jointer, etc.

4. Handling equipment for moving plaster molds and patterns. Often such patterns and molds are too heavy for manual handling. A bridge crane with an electrically operated hoist is desirable. If this is not practical, an A-frame can be used, designed to pass over the largest set-up table or plate and equipped with a chain fall or electric hoist. A fork lift truck is also useful.

Where the larger tools are being made, a bridge crane, supplemented by fork lift trucks, should be provided. In such tooling programs, plaster tools weighing 5 tons are not uncommon.

5. Adequate floor drainage, with a settling sump, should be provided in this area to permit efficient housekeeping.

6. Every plaster pattern maker should provide a complete kit of personal tools normally needed for this work. Facilities for storage and security of such tools should be provided.

Pattern- and mold-section personnel must include an adequate number of skilled plaster pattern makers who may have to be specially trained in the techniques of plaster mold making. Such men are highly skilled craftsmen. They are well worth their cost, when you consider that the accuracy of the finished plastics tool depends directly upon the accuracy of the mold from which it is made.

Welding and Metal Fabrication. Such a section is required to fabricate metal supporting structures commonly required for plastics tools, as well as metal inserts in the finished tool. Supporting structures are most economically produced by welding conventional semifinished metal mill shapes such as boiler plate, pipe or tubing, and L-bars.

Equipment required in such a section depends on the type and size of work planned, but in general, it should include:

1. Welding equipment: (a) oxyacetylene cutting equipment, both hand-operated torches and some types of pantograph; (b) arc welding equipment of adequate size to meet project requirements; (c) welding tables with heavy steel tops for weldment assembly; and (d) either manual or power-driven bending equipment capable of bending pipe and structural steel shapes.

2. Machining and heat-treating facilities may be installed or such work may be subconstructed outside the shop. Machine shop facilities may be required for more complicated types of plastic tools such as draw dies and large assembly tooling. Generally, only the basic machine tools are needed, such as engine lathe, horizontal and vertical milling equipment, radial and column drill presses, and surface grinding equipment.

Practically all metal structures used in plastics tooling must be normalized before machining in order to stabilize them. Consequently, either heat-treating facilities must be available, or arrangements must be made for subcontracting the work to an outside shop.

3. Handling equipment, both cranes and lift trucks, save time and cost in moving and locating the heavy structures frequently encountered. In many shops the same handling equipment is used by all or several sections involved.

Personnel required in this section should be mainly Class A welders and machinists accustomed to working on tooling structures, and who can adapt themselves to techniques peculiar to plastics tooling.

Mold Preparation. This section prepares the plaster molds or patterns for plastic casting or laminating, and is basically a paint shop. It must be reasonably free from dust and other foreign matter which might contaminate the mold surface.

Equipment involved includes a spray paint booth of the dry type with adequate exhaust. The size of the booth is determined by the size of tools to be painted. Spray painting equipment comparable to that generally used for auto body painting must be supplied. Such equipment requires an air compressor with filtering system to remove oil and excessive moisture from the compressed air lines. (The compressed air system may be utilized throughout the entire plastics tooling shop.)

Fireproof steel storage cabinets must be supplied for paints, lacquers and mold preparation agents which are used. Because of the flammability of the materials used, the mold preparation section is subject to the same fire hazards encountered in practically all paint shops. Local building codes and fire ordinances must be observed, as well as normal good judgment.

Personnel required are generally the same type as used in auto body painting, since similar techniques are used. Such personnel usually require little further training.

Plastics Casting. This section is used for casting both finished tools and cores. Since all tooling plastics cure by chemical reaction, this section must be equipped and organized so that no contaminating foreign substances contact the materials being cast. Consequently, dust, metallic particles, etc., must be kept to a minimum in such areas. The exact layout of this section depends on the size and type of tooling being built.

A well equipped casting area should have the following facilities:

1. *Storage racks* for barrels should be high enough to permit draining the materials directly into mixing vessels, i.e., in most cases, the valve in the drum should be about 42 inches from floor level. Racks should be mounted on casters and equipped with a floor lock to keep them stationary when in use. Steel storage cabinets should be provided for storage of smaller packages of plastics materials.

To obtain maximum usable life of stored resins, phenolics require refrigeration at 30 to 35°F. Epoxies should be stored in a cool dry place.

2. *Accurate scales and balances* are required to weigh out proper proportions of the various components of the resin system. Scales should be calibrated in ounces and have a 1000-lb maximum capacity. Balances may be standard commercial grade equipped with bronze weights calibrated in the metric system. All weighing equipment must be kept clean and periodically checked for accuracy.

3. *Handling equipment* must be available to load and unload drums on the barrel racks, to transport mixing vessels to and from the mixing equipment, and to lift casting material over the mold being filled. The exact type of equipment will depend on the physical condition of the space allocated to this section. A monorail equipped with an electric hoist of 1000-lb capacity is usually the most convenient type; frequently a merry-go-round arrangement works satisfactorily.

4. *Mixing equipment* which will provide complete and intimate mixing of components must be provided. Lightning type mixers should be pro-

vided for large mixes. Types are available for single mixes of 800 lb or 300 lb. Such equipment should be mounted on a stand equipped with a counterbalancing arrangement which will permit the agitator to operate in correct relation to the mixing vessel.

All mixing vessels, agitators, and other equipment which will contact the plastics materials should be stainless steel. An electric clock is required to time the mixing operation.

5. *A good oven,* though not always necessary, is an asset to any plastics tooling shop. The recirculated-air, indirect-fired gas type, or indirect electrically heated oven capable of maintaining temperatures ranging from 120 to 500°F, within ± 10°F, is recommended. Heat must be evenly distributed throughout the oven to avoid warpage during curing. Oven capacity and clearances depend on the type of work planned, but ovens should be of the walk-in type to reduce handling problems. Explosion-proof construction must be used throughout. Oven experts should be consulted for exact data and recommendations, particularly where local safety ordinances are involved.

6. *Casting dollies* for moving cast tools into and out of the oven should be provided. Dollies should be ruggedly built steel weldments mounted on suitable casters, and equipped with a floor lock. Dollies should be as low as possible to provide maximum head room inside the oven.

7. *Cleaning equipment* should consist of brushes and scrapers, commonly used with proper solvents to remove heavier layers of material. Steel safety cans should be provided for storage of flammable solvents. A steel tank should be provided for the strong caustic solution used to remove phenolic materials which have hardened on mixing equipment.

Personnel of the casting section should be trained to be thoroughly familiar with plastics casting techniques. They must know how to secure a mold against leaks or bursting. They should be trained to practice personel hygiene in order to avoid dermatitis and other industrial hazards that can accompany the handling of chemical compounds.

Plastics Laminating. A clean, well-lighted and ventilated area should be provided for laminating tools of glass cloth and usually epoxy resins. Required equipment includes the following:

1. *Drum racks,* similar to those required for the casting area should be provided; also steel storage cabinets for smaller packages of resin. Glass cloth and mat are usually supplied in rolls and can be dispensed in a manner similar to that used for wrapping paper. A sturdy rack capable of holding several rolls of material, one above the other, and placed adjacent to one end of the cutting table, should be supplied.

2. *Cutting and lay-up tables* should be sturdily built and equipped

with stainless steel tops. The size of the tables depends on the type of work to be done.

3. *Mechanical mixing equipment* is seldom used for laminating resins. A simple stirring rod or paddle manually operated is all that is needed in most cases. In large shops where resins are bought in bulk, stainless steel mixing vessels and adequate weighing equipment are required. Accuracy of scales and balances is important since proportioning of epoxy formulations must be held within close tolerances.

4. *Oven-curing equipment* is not necessary, but may be useful. Most epoxy laminating materials are room-temperature curing, and require non-specialized equipment. Where faster cure or maximum physical properties are required, the same curing ovens used in the casting section should be provided.

Although personnel for such a section need not be highly skilled, they should be trained to work carefully, develop a general knowledge of the type of tooling they are building, and appreciate the need for accurate work, particularly in such areas as those requiring bushings and inserts.

Tool Finishing. The tool finishing section completes all tools produced, whether cast, laminated or both. Their work consists mainly of trimming, fitting, assembling and checking the entire tool for conformance to design specifications.

Equipment required consists mainly of tool crib items, such as disk sanders, rotary files, and hand routers. All minor repairs and alterations to casts and laminates are made by this group.

Personnel must be experienced, skilled tool engineers who know the entire plastics tooling operation and what is required of a tool in order that it function properly. They must be provided with work benches and adequate storage facilities for personal tools and equipment.

Tool Proofing. This section is used to test or "proof" the tool in either actual production equipment or simulated equipment. Such equipment as draw presses, stretch presses, hydropresses, etc. are often involved.

Personnel should consist of tool and die makers with broad enough experience to enable them to alter a given tool so that it will function properly, and co-ordinate with other tooling involved.

Service Facilities. In practically all plastics tool shops a central tool and supply crib is most economical. Such cribs must be stocked with adequate precision cubes, knees, straight edges, height gages, vernier scales and the accessory equipment normally needed in conjunction with these tools. A stock of hand tools, cutting tools, etc., required to do the actual work must be maintained.

The same section will also store and dispense shop supplies. It is also

of fabrication to be used, and (3) type of materials to be used. Basically, casting materials are estimated on volume cost/cu in.; laminates are figured by the square foot with relation to the thickness of laminate and variable contours involved. Labor on flat lay-up laminating runs about 20 to 25 sq ft/man hour. More intricate shapes and contour may run twice that amount. The best procedure for accurately estimating costs is to study individual workers in your own shop and estimate their productivity in terms of salary for your particular type of worker in your geographic locality.

REFERENCES

1. Delmonte, J., "Control of Physical Properties," paper presented at 25th Anniversary Meeting, American Society of Tool Engineers, March 1957.
2. Hankins, N. R., "Plastics Materials Most Suitable for Tooling and Organizing to Use Them Successfully," paper presented at Purdue University Seminar on Plastics Tooling, June 1959.
3. Oye, L. J., Rezolin, Inc., personal communication.

3. *Plastics versus Other Tooling Materials*

An engineer selecting a material is concerned with performance; in addition he wants a material that can be put into the shape he needs easily and efficiently. The indexes used to describe performance are engineering properties. However, they are only indexes of how a material will behave under specific conditions.

When a unified science of materials matures, materials selection will ideally be based on fundamental structure, and what it provides in the way of performance, fabricability and cost, with no reference as to whether the material is a "metal," a "plastic," or a "ceramic." At present, however, we still have relatively clearly defined and separate materials sciences. And too often those involved in one of these sciences are ill-informed (or misinformed) about another. This problem is particularly acute in the plastics field because of the rapid development of an amazingly large amount of plastics technology. Anyone working in another technology is hard-pressed to keep informed in such a rapidly growing field.

The purpose of this chapter is to orient those unfamiliar with plastics to these materials—and in particular those plastics used for tooling—and to point out the important differences in behavior between plastics and conventional tooling materials. Also, some of the commonly misinterpreted properties of plastics will be explained to help the tool engineer properly evaluate published data on plastics.

What Plastics Are

Plastics are giant molecules, or high polymers. They consist of basic simple repeating chemical structural units called *mers* or *monomers*. When these monomers are joined together to form a long chain or giant molecule (by a polymerization process), the resulting "plastic" is called a *polymer.* Actually, the differences between high-molecular-weight polymeric materials and low-molecular-weight materials are largely physical. For example, ethylene with a molecular weight of 28 is a gas; polyethylene produced by a high-pressure polymerization process to yield a material of high molecular weight of about 20,000 is a soft, flexible plastic, or high polymer. Molecular size, shape and structure rather than chemical analysis separate the gas from the plastic.

There is a large number of high polymers or plastics, each plastics family being identified by the chemical type of repeating unit within the polymer's long-chain molecules; e.g., polyethylenes are identified by repeating ethylene mers, polypropylenes by repeating propylene mers, polyesters by repeating ester linkages, epoxies by recurring epoxide groups, etc.

Another factor that plays a strong part in determining properties of a plastic material is the geometric relationship of the mer units in the chain. For example, in linear polymers, mers are hooked end-to-end in long, relatively straight chains. Linear branched polymers are long, relatively straight chains with side chains of atom groups or radicals extending from the straight chain. (The well-publicized "ordered" or "isotactic" polymers—polypropylene, for one—are linear branched polymers in which the side chains are located at specific predetermined points along and around the chain equidistant from each other.)

Linear copolymers are long, straight chains in which two different chemical types of mers are hooked up in the chain. Graft copolymers are those in which the basic long chain is of one type of mer, with long-chain "grafts" of the other type of mer extending from the base chain. Block copolymers are those in which "blocks" of repeating mers are hooked end-to-end and inserted in a long chain of different types of mers.

All these geometric types of polymers discussed above are essentially thermoplastic. The chains are packed into the material, either in random configurations such as amorphous polystyrene, or in varying degrees of orientation. The strength of amorphous thermoplastic materials is primarily dependent on the secondary bond forces (van der Waals) between the chains.

Crystalline thermoplastics, e.g., polyethylene, nylon, are those materials in which areas of each polymer chain become closely aligned with areas of other polymer chains, these areas of alignment forming crystals. Portions of chains which extend into crystalline areas are very close to other chains in the crystallite; consequently, the secondary forces are high. In most crystalline polymers, crystallinity is partial. Evidence indicates that in such materials, individual polymer molecules pass successively through several crystalline and amorphous regions. This is believed to account for the superior strength properties of crystalline, as opposed to amorphous, polymers.

In all these thermoplastics, since the forces holding the material in shape are secondary forces, the materials repeatedly soften when heated and harden on cooling. Theoretically this softening and hardening can be repeated indefinitely if the temperature does not become high enough to degrade or break the polymer chains.

On the other hand, a thermosetting plastic will not soften appreciably up to its decomposition temperature. Such a plastic has a linear, relatively low-molecular-weight thermoplastic polymer chain with "cross-links" which bond the long chains together with primary valence bonds (which are orders of magnitude stronger than secondary bonds). Such a three-dimensional, highly cross-linked polymer is of very high and indeterminant molecular weight, and generally rigid. Actually these materials can be produced with properties ranging from rubber-like to highly rigid depending on the number and lengths of the cross-linking chains, and the size and nature of the so-called main chain.

Tooling plastics such as epoxies, phenolics and polyesters are all thermosetting materials. When purchased in liquid form they are mixed with curing agents, hardeners or catalysts, which cause polymerization and cross-linking to form strong, infusible solids.

Effects of Processing

When you buy a tooling metal, it is either in ingot or semifinished form. In making the tool, the metal is either melted and cast, or mechanically worked or machined to form the finished shape. Consequently, there is little, if any, difference in the composition and properties of the metal as-purchased and the metal in the completed tool. The producer of the metal has predetermined its properties by alloying or processing it to its as-purchased form.

When you buy a tooling plastic, it is usually in the form of a liquid (or paste) resin (a partially polymerized monomer)—or, basically, a chemical compound. In making the tool, the resin is mixed with other chemicals and often solid materials such as fillers or reinforcements, and is cast or laminated to the finished shape. Chemical reactions within the material actually change the material, producing its final performance capabilities. From one standpoint, you are actually making the material, along with the tool.

This is an important difference between metals and plastics, because the mixing, formulating and curing of the plastics determine to a great extent the properties of the finished material—just as the alloying of the metal in the producers plant has a determining effect on properties of the alloy. Consequently the engineer must know a great deal more about the basic chemical technology of plastics than he had to know about the alloying of metals. The subsequent chapters on materials and fabricating techniques attempt to clarify this area of technology. For more detailed information references at the ends of appropriate chapters should be consulted.

Behavior Differences

From the behavior standpoint, one of the important differences between plastics and metals is the sensitivity of plastics to the effects of time. Consequently they are much more sensitive than metals to rate of stressing, and aging under various environmental conditions. In spite of the newness of plastics, a substantial amount of design information is available. But long periods of time required for testing to determine effects of long-time use have limited the amount of data on creep, fatigue and long-time exposure to heat and chemicals.

Engineering properties as determined by standard test procedures are the only practical measure we have of predicting the behavior of a material in service. The engineering properties of plastics most pertinent to tooling use include (1) mechanical properties (both short-term and long-term), such as strength, hardness, and wear resistance, and their relationship to physical properties such as density and moisture absorption; (2) thermal characteristics, such as heat resistance, thermal conductivity and thermal expansion characteristics; and (3) chemical resistance.

Mechanical Properties. The standard ASTM (American Society for Testing Materials) tests for determining mechanical properties are quite similar in concept to those for metals. These tests are spelled out in *ASTM Standards, Part 6*, i.e., Tensile Properties of Plastics D638, Flexural Properties of Plastics D790, Compressive Properties of Rigid Plastics D659, Bearing Strength of Plastics D953, Shear Strength of Plastics D732, etc.

There is a substantial difference in strength between unreinforced and reinforced plastics. An unreinforced cast epoxy resin, for example may have a tensile strength of 8000 to 12,000 psi, a flexural strength of about 15,000 to 22,000 psi, and tensile modulus of elasticity of 400,000 to 500,000 psi. Fabric-reinforced epoxy laminates have tensile strengths of about 40,000 to 60,000 psi, flexural strengths of 60,000 to 80,000 psi, and tensile moduli of elasticity of about 3 to 4 million psi. Consequently, the term "high-strength plastics," usually refers to reinforced plastics.

A basic difference in strength characteristics between metals and reinforced plastics is direction of strength. Metals have essentially isotropic strength characteristics (though working of wrought metals provides a degree of directionality). Reinforced plastics are essentially anisotropic, strength being greatest in the direction of the primary load-bearing constituent, i.e., the glass or metal fibers.

The strength of reinforced plastics is dependent not only on the strength of the reinforcing fiber, but also on the strength of the bond between resin and fiber. Also, the over-all load-bearing ability of such a composite is dependent on the highly complex stress and strain distributions within the mass.

Ultimate strengths of tooling laminates are for the most part lower than those of metals. For example, though tensile strengths of glass cloth-epoxy laminates (in the strongest direction) may be comparable with the 30,000 to 80,000 psi values for aluminum alloys and the 50,000 to 70,000 psi values for cast iron, they are substantially lower than the 120,000 to 150,000 psi of nodular or ductile iron and the 150,000 to 190,000 psi of hardened and tempered high-carbon steels.

More outstanding is the difference in rigidity or modulus of elasticity between tooling plastics and metals. Compared with a 3 to 4 million psi tensile modulus of glass cloth-epoxy laminates, aluminum has a tensile modulus of about 10 million psi, cast iron has a tensile modulus of 18 to 20 million psi, nodular or ductile cast iron has a modulus of about 22 to 25 million psi, and high-carbon steels have moduli of about 29 to 30 million psi.

The importance of reinforced plastics from the strength standpoint lies in their strength-weight relationship. An epoxy-glass cloth laminate has an average density of about 0.064 lb/cu in. (1.78 specific gravity), compared with 0.26 to 0.28 lb/cu in. (7.2 to 7.7 specific gravity) for irons and steels. Consequently, although reinforced laminates must be used in greater thickness to obtain the rigidity and strength of steel or iron, even at this greater thickness, the section is lighter in weight.

Whether a plastics material will serve in a load-bearing tool can be determined only after a careful analysis of the magnitude and directionality of the stresses to be imposed on the tool, and the economics in providing a plastic material that will withstand these stresses in the direction required.

Also to be considered are the number of variables affecting strength of the reinforced plastics tool. Although there are too many variables to attempt a complete listing, some of the important ones include:

1. *Ratio of Resin to Reinforcement.* In general, for glass cloth-reinforced laminates, highest glass content provides optimum tensile strengths; lowest glass content, optimum compressive properties; and a compromise in content provides optimum flexural properties. The relationship differs somewhat with mat reinforcement. Figure 3.1 shows these effects qualitatively. Optimum properties for tooling laminates are generally obtained at about 50:50 reinforcement-resin ratio.

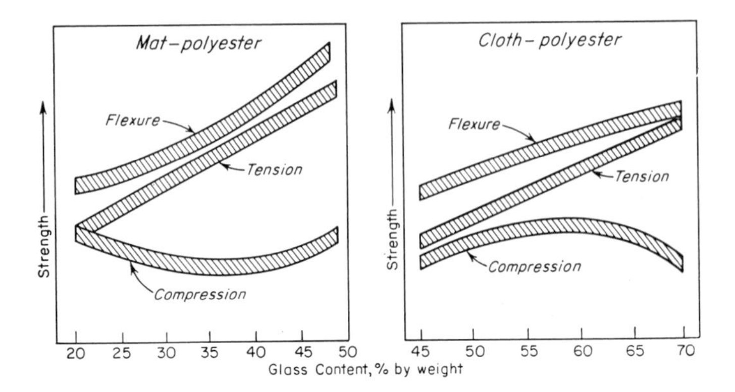

Figure 3.1. Qualitative effects of glass content on mat and cloth-reinforced polyester laminates. (*Sonneborn*)

2. *Effect of Laminate Thickness.* Density and thickness of a laminate depend primarily on type of reinforcement, molding method and technique. For a given laminate, however, no true correlation has been developed to indicate the effect of changing thickness on properties. Data on thin laminates vary considerably among different sources. Some tests indicate increasing strengths with decreasing thicknesses; others indicate decreasing strengths with decreasing thicknesses. Evidently, the effects are due to some characteristics of the material that are not yet understood.

3. *Orientation of Reinforcing Fibers.* As mentioned before, directionality of reinforcement is critical in determining strength of a laminate. Strength follows the direction of the reinforcement.

Stresses acting on a part in service are rarely unidirectional. Consequently, strength values derived from testing in only one direction on a laminate (usually in the warp direction) are rarely sufficient to develop a realistic design. Strength of the laminate in various directions other than

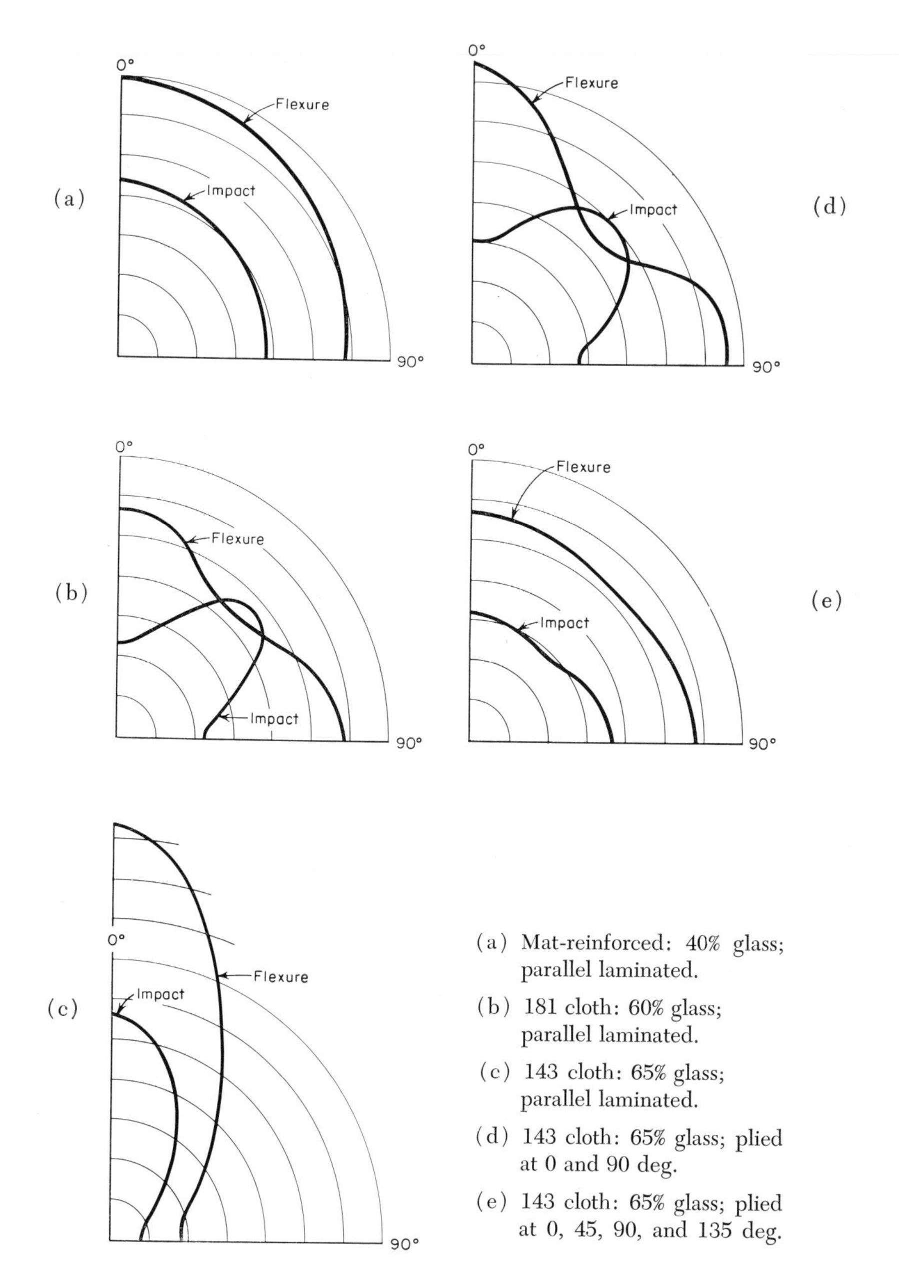

(a) Mat-reinforced: 40% glass; parallel laminated.

(b) 181 cloth: 60% glass; parallel laminated.

(c) 143 cloth: 65% glass; parallel laminated.

(d) 143 cloth: 65% glass; plied at 0 and 90 deg.

(e) 143 cloth: 65% glass; plied at 0, 45, 90, and 135 deg.

Figure 3.2. Effect of fiber orientation on flexural and impact strengths of glass-reinforced laminates. Equations are available for determining specific values at any given degree from warp, given zero and 90 deg. values. (*Sonneborn*)

the warp direction must usually be known to design a part that is to undergo critical stresses in service.

Figure 3.2 shows qualitatively the directional properties of a mat and four fabric-reinforced laminates. The concentric arcs represent different impact and flexural strength levels, strengths increasing with distance from the origin. Degrees are degrees from warp direction, "0" degrees being parallel with warp. The opposite three quadrants not shown will display the same strength patterns.

Figure 3.2a shows mat-reinforced laminates to be relatively isotropic, though strengths are relatively low. The 181 fabric (satin weave) shown in Figure 3.2b is bidirectional, having lower values for flexural strength and higher values for impact at 45 degrees to the warp direction. Figure 3.2c shows the directional characteristics provided by a 143 fabric which has about 90 per cent of its yarns in the warp direction. Figures 3.2d and 3.2e show different strength configurations obtainable by alternately orienting different plies in slightly different directions.

Actually, most laminated tooling today is made with a simple plain-weave fabric. This is laid up in alternating plies to provide essentially isotropic strength characteristics to the laminate. The benefits obtainable by designing a tool with different strength in different directions, depending on the stress requirements of the tool, are obvious.

Plastics are softer than metals (being measured usually on the Rockwell M scale), and generally have poorer wear resistance. Wear or abrasion resistance is a difficult property to measure, resistance being highly dependent on many variables such as type of abradant, speed and direction of abrasion, pressures involved, etc. Although a so-called Tabor abrasion tester is often used to evaluate plastics, results of such tests are not indicative of service performance, and may even be misleading when used for comparisons. Usually where severe abrasion conditions are anticipated in a tool, metal or carbide inserts are used.

From the tooling standpoint, the major importance of the moisture absorption of a plastic material (ASTM D570) is the effect of the moisture on properties. The effects of wet conditioning depend on the resin and the finish used on the reinforcement. Exposures of up to one year in high humidity have reduced flexural strengths of laminates by 20 to 30 per cent. Reduced strength data given in Chapters 4 and 5 are for materials after exposure to moisture.

As mentioned before, plastics are sensitive to duration of loading. The effects vary and definitive data are not available for all types of laminates. The major differences between reinforced plastics and metals in time-dependent properties are as follows:

1. *Fatigue.* Most metals, under conditions of cyclic stressing, reach an endurance limit after which continued stress cycling produces no further reduction in strength. Reinforced plastics do not generally exhibit this behavior. Continued application of cyclic stresses continues to reduce effective strength. Some data on this effect are given in Chapter 4.

2. *Creep and Stress Rupture.* Metals have relatively low creep and good stress-rupture strength at room temperature. In fabric-reinforced laminates, tensile creep appears to be negligible at room temperature, both in

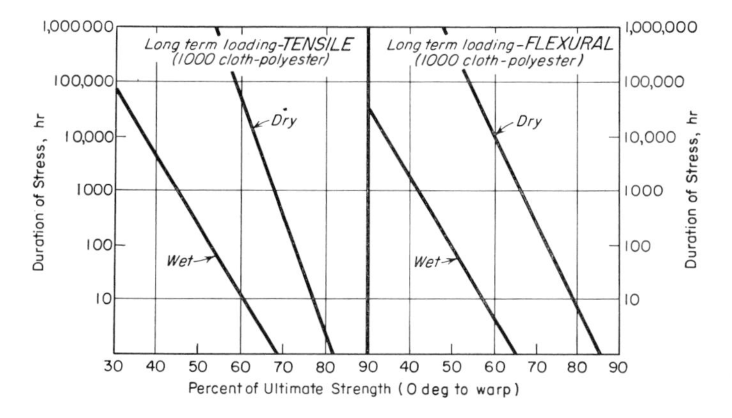

Figure 3.3. Effect of long-term loading on tensile and flexural strengths of a glass-polyester laminate. (*Gibbs & Cox*)

the parallel and perpendicular to warp directions, although initial deformations are on the order of 0.75 to 1.75 per cent. Although initial strain for mat-reinforced laminates is much lower than for fabric-based laminates, creep in mat laminates appears to be substantially higher.

Unlike deformation, tensile-load-carrying-ability (stress-rupture characteristics) of cloth-based laminates is markedly reduced by the length of time under load. This reduction can vary from about 30 to 70 per cent of the short-time ultimate strength, depending on duration of load. Figure 3.3 shows this relationship under both wet and dry conditions for a 1000 cloth (plain weave) reinforced polyester laminate under both tensile and flexural loading conditions, expressed as percentage of short-term ultimate *vs.* duration of load.

Thermal Properties. Standard ASTM tests for measuring commonly reported thermal properties of plastics are Heat Distortion Temperature of Plastics D648, Deformation of Plastics Under Load D621, and Coefficient of Linear Thermal Expansion, D264.

The major thermal differences between plastics and metals include the much lower degree of thermal stability of plastics, their much higher thermal expansion characteristics, and their much lower thermal conductivity.

One of the most difficult properties of a material to evaluate is its heat resistance. The maximum temperature to which a material can be exposed is solely dependent on such factors as the type and magnitude of stressing during exposure, length of exposure, and the degree of degradation permissible before the material ceases to function satisfactorily. For example, reinforced plastics are used in ablative type re-entry missile nose cones only because the duration of exposure to the 15,000 to 25,000°F temperatures is extremely short (a few seconds to a few minutes), and because of the endothermic nature of the chemical reactions which occur as the plastics material pyrolyzes at these temperatures.

The most commonly reported heat resistance values for plastics are "heat-distortion temperatures" and "maximum recommended service temperatures." These values are often misinterpreted. Values for heat-distortion temperature indicate only the temperatures at which a standard specimen of the material deflects an arbitrary standard amount under either of two standard loads, i.e., either 66- or 264-psi fiber stress. Test results should always state the load for which the value is reported, although for thermosetting resins 264 psi stress is most commonly used.

There is no standard test for maximum recommended service temperature. Most such data are general values based on experience, and have no consistent correlation with heat-distortion temperatures, which are short-time tests. Either of these values should be used only for comparing two or more materials in a general way. For example, a material may have a heat-distortion temperature of 250°F, but the effects of continued time at temperature may limit the maximum use temperature to 180°F.

The most useful type of heat resistance data are those indicating specific mechanical properties of the material after heat aging, with measurements being made at the aging temperature. Unfortunately this type of data is rare. Heat aging itself requires a substantial amount of time, and equipment for conducting tests at high temperatures is costly.

Plastics are essentially thermal insulators while metals are thermal conductors. Thermal conductivity of unfilled plastics is about 1 to 4 Btu/hr/sq ft/°F/in., compared with about 117 for stainless steel, 320 for carbon steel, 728 for Kirksite, and 990 to 1160 for aluminum. The lower thermal conductivity can be advantageous in many plastics applications, but it is an important disadvantage in many tooling applications. First, it insulates the surface of the tool, concentrating any externally generated heat in local areas of the tool surface. Also, in heated molds, such as used in plastics forming, it severely limits the distribution and uniformity of distribution of heat over the mold surface. Filling and reinforcing the resin with conductive fibers and powders can substantially improve thermal conduction, as described later.

The substantially higher thermal expansion of plastics (e.g., 25 to $35 \times 10^{-6}/°F$ for a cast epoxy, versus 6 to $8 \times 10^{-6}/°F$ for cast iron and steel) must be kept in mind in designing, particularly in those tools consisting of combinations of metals and plastics. Laminating plastics with glass cloth substantially reduce this expansivity (to about 8 to 9×10^{-6}).

Chemical Resistance. The standard ASTM chemical resistance test is Resistance of Plastics to Chemical Reagents D543. Results are reported in terms of percentage gain or loss of weight and dimensional change after total immersion for 7 days at 73°F. As is the case with heat resistance, chemical resistance is dependent on many variables, including type and concentration of reagent, temperature and duration of exposure, type of exposure (e.g., immersion, one-side exposure, splash exposure, exposure to fumes only, etc.), and degree of degradation permissible.

The fact remains that plastics in general have exceptionally good resistance to chemicals, as compared with metals. Beyond this generalization, specific data should be obtained from materials suppliers.

REFERENCES

1. "Marine Design Manual for Fiberglass Reinforced Plastics," Directed by Gibbs & Cox, Inc., sponsored by Owens-Corning Fiberglas Corp., McGraw-Hill Publishing Co., Inc., New York, 1960.
2. Materials Selector Issue, *Materials in Design Engineering*, 1959-60.
3. Morgan, P., "Glass Reinforced Plastics," London, Iliffe & Sons, Ltd., 1957.
4. "Plastics Engineering Handbook of The Society of The Plastics Industry," 3rd ed., New York, Reinhold Publishing Corp., 1960.
5. "Proposed Test Methods for Laminating Resin Systems," Document 1 SPI-PTL SPI Plastics for Tooling Div., Oct. 1957.
6. Riley, M. W., "Low Pressure Reinforced Plastics," *Materials in Design Engineering* (Feb. 1960).
7. Sonneborn, R. G., "Fiberglas Reinforced Plastics," New York, Reinhold Publishing Corp., 1954.
8. "Test Methods for Cast Plastic Tooling Materials," Document SPI-PTD-1 SPI Plastics for Tooling Div., Apr. 1957.

4. *Epoxy Resins*

Epoxy resins are the most widely used tooling plastics. Although more costly than phenolics or polyesters, when properly fabricated they provide superior strength, toughness and dimensional stability, much lower shrinkage, superior chemical resistance, excellent adhesion, good wetting of reinforcing materials, and the ability to be room-temperature cured. In addition, they are versatile in that they can be cast, laminated, troweled or splined.

One of the most common uses for tooling plastics has been as glass-reinforced laminates for surfacing all types of tools. Resins have also been cast to form both tool faces and cores or backing structures. Metal powder- or chopped glass-filled pastes or putties are used for repair, caulking, and splining. One of the most promising new approaches is the use of metal fiber-filled high-temperature epoxy, both for tool surfaces and/or pressure-cast core or backing structures.

This chapter outlines the basic chemistry of epoxy resins, the curing agents which can be used, the forms in which epoxies are used, and properties obtainable. The discussion is intended not only to cover the types presently used, but also to indicate types which may, under certain conditions, present definite benefits in the future, e.g., higher-temperature epoxy resins. Bear in mind that at present, by far the most common epoxy systems are the bisphenol A resins and modifications thereof, combined with amine hardeners. The excellent room-temperature handling characteristics provided by amine curing agents have limited most tooling fabrication to such systems.

Much of the chemistry in this chapter has been adapted from Lee and Neville [2] and Skeist,[6] both excellent sources of more detailed information for those interested.

Chemical Structure

Uncured epoxy resins are thermoplastic materials containing one or more of the reactive epoxy groups:

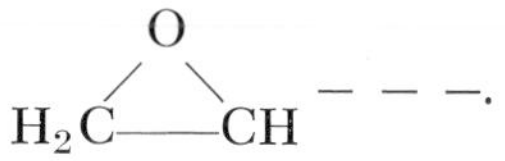

$$\begin{array}{c} \quad O \\ \ \ / \quad \backslash \\ H_2C\text{——}CH \end{array} - - - .$$

Molecules containing such groups are capable of reacting with other chemicals to form larger molecules. Essentially, the size of the resulting molecule and the number of cross-links between molecular chains determines the characteristics of the final resin.

Molecules in liquid resins are relatively small. Appropriate hardeners either act as catalysts in homopolymerizing the resin, or the hardeners enter the reaction themselves with the resin to form the cured thermosetting mass.

Most commercial epoxy resins are the reaction product of epichlorohydrin and bisphenol A. By varying the ratio of these chemicals, resins are produced which range in molecular weight from about 350 to 4000. They vary in physical form from liquids to high-melting solids. The resin used in plastics tooling is usually the liquid type, which is essentially the diglycidyl ether of bisphenol A. Its viscosity is reduced for easier handling by the addition of reactive diluents such as butyl glycidyl or phenyl glycidyl ether. Such resins are reactive with a variety of hardeners and curing agents, and provide a range of properties dependent on formulation. Most epoxies in the subsequent discussions are of this type.

More recently, several other epoxies have been developed, most of them designed to provide superior heat resistance, and some to provide lower cost in the finished product.

Epoxy novolac resins (reaction products of epichlorohydrin and a phenolic resin) have been produced for some time. They provide better thermal stability than the bisphenol A epoxies, but high viscosity has presented processing difficulties and composition has been difficult to control. Recently developed epoxy novolac resins (Dow Chemical Co.) appear promising, but viscosities are still high. Although heat aging data are limited, the resins appear to retain good strengths after exposure to 500°F temperatures.

Epoxy resins based on the peracetic acid-derived diepoxides developed by Union Carbide Chemicals (announced in late 1958) combine high functionality with low viscosity. They offer higher heat distortion points than conventional epoxies. Formulating of resins based on these chemicals is still in its early stages, but even further improvements in heat resistance are expected. One formulation, VC-8359, developed by Brunswick Corp. has been approved for Type II (500°F) parts under MIL-R-9300-A. More details are given later.

In early 1960, Food Machinery and Chemicals Corp. (FMC) announced a new family of epoxy resins (chemically, epoxidized polybutadienes). Although such resins provide lighter weight and improved heat resistance, the important benefits of the materials would seem to stem from their reactivity. In addition to epoxy groups the resin molecule has reactive hydroxyl groups, providing generally a higher degree of reactivity, and also a different type of reactivity. The resins are reactive with peroxide curing agents, as well as common epoxy curing agents. Also, they are more reactive with anhydride curing agents at lower temperatures, and more sluggish in reaction with amines. This can provide, on the one hand, more easily processed anhydride systems (providing heat-resistant systems), and on the other hand, amine systems with better pot life.

The systems also can make use of higher proportions of low cost anhydride/glycol curing systems (e.g., maleic anhydride/propylene glycol). According to FMC, in glass-reinforced laminates, such systems may result in over-all cured-materials costs closer to those of polyesters than to those of epoxies.

Resin Characteristics

There are several basic characteristics of liquid epoxy resins that serve as indexes of the behavior and usefulness of the materials. Two of the most important are viscosity and epoxide equivalent.

Viscosity is a useful index of handling properties, as well as molecular weight. The most commonly used epoxy resins have viscosities of about 8000 to 20,000 cps. For example, Shell Chemical's "Epon" 828 resin has a viscosity of 5000 to 15,000 cps; Union Carbide's ERL-2774 has a viscosity range of 10,500 to 19,500 cps. Much lower viscosity resins are also available, and where lower viscosities are desired in certain resins reactive diluents can be used.

Epoxide equivalent and epoxy value are used to indicate the reactivity of the resin. Epoxide equivalent is the weight of resin in grams which contains 1 gram chemical equivalent of epoxy. Low-molecular-weight resins have epoxide equivalent ranges of about 175 to 200; higher weight resins have correspondingly higher values since in each such molecule there are longer chains between the epoxy groups. If the resin chains are assumed (1) to be linear with no side branching and (2) to have epoxy groups terminating the ends of each chain, the epoxide equivalent (weight) is one-half the average molecular weight of the resin.

The term *epoxy value* is also used. It represents the fractional number of epoxy groups contained in 100 grams of resin. The two terms are essentially equivalent. Dividing the epoxy value into 100 gives the epoxide equivalent.

Epoxide equivalents of commonly used resins are: "Epon" 828, 175 to 210; "ERL"-2774, 175 to 200; Ciba's "Araldite" 6020, about 210. One of the important improvements in liquid epoxy resins lies in the improved accuracy (narrower range) with which epoxide equivalents can be specified by materials suppliers. Ranges given for a liquid resin are becoming narrower, permitting the end user to more accurately determine such compounding variables as optimum proportion of hardening agents, etc.

Hardeners and Curing Agents

Use of the proper type and proportion of hardening agent or catalyst is essential not only to obtain the final properties required, but also in providing the processing characteristics desired. On the one hand, pot life must be long enough to permit mixing a large enough batch to accomplish the fabrication; on the other hand, pot life must be short enough to permit economical curing cycles—particularly where room-temperature cures are desired.

Epoxy resins are cured by a variety of compounds containing active hydrogen, or by a catalyzed self-reaction. The materials in the former group, usually called *hardeners,* coreact with the resin to become an integral part of the cured material. The catalysts promote the self-polymerization of the epoxy resin. Following are brief descriptions of the most important types of curing agents.

Primary and Secondary Aliphatic Amines. The primary and secondary aliphatic amines are hardeners, and are the most widely used for curing tooling epoxies. They are relatively low-viscosity liquids which are quite reactive at room temperature, providing good room-temperature mixing and handling characteristics, and the ability to be cured at room temperature. Elevated-temperature postcures of about 2 hr at 212°F improve properties. Although a typical heat-distortion temperature for such a system might be about 212°F (264 psi load), such systems are not usually recommended for use at temperatures much above 180°F.

Typical aliphatic amine curing agents include diethylenetriamine, triethylenetetramine, monoethanolamine, and diethylaminopropylamine. Although most unmodified aliphatic amine hardeners are skin irritants, modified types or so-called safety hardeners are available which provide minimum skin irritation. Modified types are also available with altered pot lives, curing rates and viscosities.

Aromatic Amines. Aromatic amines provide higher temperature resistance (heat distortion values of about 300°F), and substantially superior solvent and chemical resistance than aliphatic amines, but are seldom used for tooling. Most aromatic amines are solids at room temperature. They must be dispersed in the liquid epoxy at elevated temperatures. They are also available as liquid eutectic blends at room temperature, but all require elevated temperatures to gel and postcure the resins. Also, catalysts such as boron trifluoride monoethylamine must normally be used.

Typical aromatic amines include *p,p'*-methylenedianiline, *m'*-phenylenediamine, and diaminodiphenyl sulfone.

Acid Anhydrides. Anhydrides as a class provide the maximum heat resistance in epoxy systems. They are little if at all used in tooling because (1) most are solids at room temperature, and must be heated to 95 to 250°F, depending on the type, to liquefy them, and (2) although liquid anhydrides, such as methyl nadic anhydride, are liquid at room temperature, they require heat to gel and cure them.

Because anhydrides react sluggishly with bisphenol A type epoxies at room temperatures, they provide long pot life, in some cases as long as 2 weeks or more. However, although longer pot life is useful in handling the resin, it means excessively long cure times at room temperature.

Other typical anhydride curing agents include pyromelitic dianhydride, chlorendic (HET) anhydride, maleic anhydride, and phthalic anhydride.

Flexibilizing Modifiers and Hardeners. Such hardeners are compounded with epoxies to reduce brittleness and to provide varying degrees of flexibility. Also, they can be used to eliminate the need for toxic aliphatic amine hardeners.

The two most common flexibilizing agents are the polyamides such as General Mills' "Versamid" resins, and liquid polysulfide elastomers such as Thiokol Chemical's "LP-3." The lower viscosity "Versamids" can be blended with liquid epoxies and cured at room temperatures, although mild elevated temperatures quicken cure and develop optimum properties. Polysulfide liquid polymers are used in conjunction with tertiary amine catalysts or aliphatic amine hardeners. Systems are usually low in viscosity, and will cure at room temperature, although elevated temperatures may be used with slow catalysts to provide optimum pot life, and develop the best physical properties.

A recently announced (early 1960) low-viscosity (15 to 20 cps) flexible hardener appears promising for tooling. Coatings made with the new hardener (designated "ZZLA" 0822 by Union Carbide Plastics) can be bent over 1/8 in. mandrels without cracking, yet castings and laminates are rigid at room temperature. It can be combined with "Thiokol" LP-3 to make tough, rubbery molds or die facings.

Other flexible hardeners are the "Duomeen" hardener produced by Armour, Cardolite filling material (not actually a hardener) produced by Minnesota Mining, and the blends of fatty acid dimers and trimers produced by Emery Industries. Duomeens are liquids or pastes which are dissolved in the resin. The systems have low viscosities, and mild elevated-temperature postcures are usually used to obtain optimum properties. Cardolite compounds are fillers containing reactive epoxide groups which react with the hardener employed in the system. They can be used with a wide range of hardeners, and provide toughness by a plasticizing action. The fatty acid dimer and trimer blends are usually mixed with the epoxy, gelled and cured at elevated temperatures. Tertiary amine catalysts are usually recommended to accelerate cure.

Catalytic Hardeners. Catalysts can be used to self-polymerize the epoxy resin. They can be used in varying proportions to control pot life and cure rate.

Acidic catalysts include boron trifluoride amine complexes, such as boron trifluoride monoethylamine. They have limited activity at room temperature, providing long pot life. Cured with heat, they can provide heat distortion temperatures as high as 320°F.

The most commonly used type of alkaline catalyst are the tertiary amines, such as triethylamine, diethylaminepropylamine, dimethylaminomethyl phenol, tridimethylaminomethyl phenol, and benzyldimethylamine. They can provide long pot life, as well as room-temperature curing characteristics. Mild elevated-temperature postcures are usually employed to develop optimum properties.

The above classification of curing agents is obviously oversimplified. Both base resin suppliers and tooling plastics formulators offer specific recommendations for type and quantities of curing agents to be used with their materials.

Handling Epoxies

In commercial handling of epoxies, there are several important factors to be considered. Summarizing briefly from Lee and Neville,[2] these are:

1. Fillers should generally be added in a separate compounding operation, well in advance of production (or filled resin formulations may be purchased initially). Optimum results require heating fillers to drive off water; after filling, the resin mix should be either allowed to stand until bubbles have escaped, or deaerated by vacuum.

2. Since best results are obtained by careful weighing of curing agents, production metering devices should be provided.

3. Optimum batch size must be determined, based on the type of curing agent used and the temperature at which the system is worked. Usually, resin systems maintain workable viscosities for most of their pot life; once appreciable exotherm is generated, however, gelation occurs rapidly. Size of batch will determine pot life. With the more reactive amines, batches are usually 1 to 2 lb, or sometimes as large as 5 lb. A system of batch replenishment may be used, involving the periodic addition of freshly catalyzed mix to the material being worked.

4. Suitable stirring and application equipment must be available.

5. Health hazards must be eliminated or properly countervailed. Many liquid epoxy resins and the curing agents used are primary skin irritants. Amine curing agents, for instance, are generally the most irritating. They can be considered as strong caustics, and will produce serious local injury on short exposure. Also, they may sensitize individuals so that even slight future exposure can cause skin irritation. The acid anhydrides, like other organic acids, will cause burns if allowed to remain in prolonged contact with the skin. Also, some reactive diluents are particularly irritating. The irritation potential of the liquid resin itself, while present, is of considerably less consequence.

Although this health problem has been relatively well publicized, little has been said about successful solutions to the problem. The fact remains that epoxy resins are being safely used every day. The point to remember is that precautions must be taken. As discussed elsewhere (see Chapter 2), skin contact should be avoided, adequate ventilation must be provided in the shop, and personal hygiene must be practiced. There are also so-called safety hardeners which have been developed to minimize this problem. Materials suppliers can give details on these materials.

6. Suitable release agents must be used to permit stripping of cured parts from their molds. Epoxy resins are excellent adhesives, consequently proper release agents are critical. Release agents may be of the coating type, such as waxes or silicone liquids or greases, or of the film type, such as polyvinyl alcohol, polyethylene, TFE-fluorocarbon, or cellophane. The selection of the proper type depends on the mold, as well as other variables. The subject is discussed in more detail in Chapter 7.

Fillers

The major use of fillers and short-fiber reinforcements is in casting resin formulations, surface coats, and pastes or putties. Fillers may be added to reduce cost, lower coefficient of thermal expansion, reduce shrinkage, increase thermal conductivity, alter surface hardness, reduce exotherms, improve adhesive properties and/or alter handling characteristics of the resin system. Short-fiber reinforcement (e.g., glass or metal) may affect several of these characteristics, but they are also used to provide additional strength to the cured material. Figure 4.1 is indicative of the variations in handling characteristics obtainable with fillers.

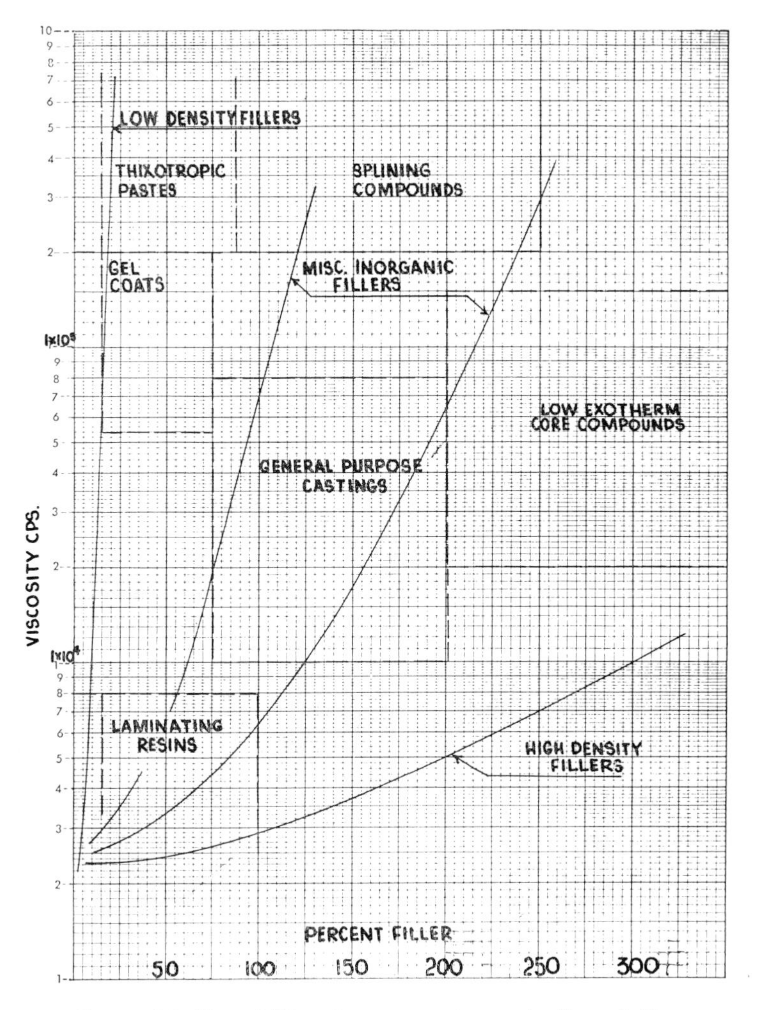

Figure 4.1. Use of fillers in epoxy resins, and effect of filler on viscosity. (*Furane Plastics, Inc.*)

The selection of the proper type, particle size and proportion of filler is a complex science in itself. However, in brief, the following characteristics can be obtained by use of fillers.

Lower Cost. Sand, calcium carbonate and many other inert fillers are negligible in cost compared to resin and hardener. Cost benefits are particularly significant in large mass castings. But fillers also alter properties. Reducing cost by filler addition is fine only if required performance is not sacrificed.

Lower Exotherm. Thicknesses of more than ¼ in. of unfilled epoxy resin may result in excessive build-up of heat. Since the resin is an excellent thermal insulator, such heat is not dissipated, and if it reaches too high a temperature some of the more volatile ingredients in the interior of the casting may boil, causing voids or surface imperfections.

The more filler added, the lower is the exotherm generated. Also, if the filler has high thermal conductivity (e.g., aluminum powder) it will help dissipate heat from the core of the material. According to Skeist,[6] the exotherm developed during cure of a composition containing 75 per cent filler will be only about one-fourth of that generated by unfilled composition.

Although thermally conductive fillers increase conductivity of the filled material, the particles are still discrete, each surrounded by a shell of insulating resin. Consequently, even highly filled compositions still have a relatively low degree of conductivity. Where thermal conductivity is critical, incorporation of continuous conductors, such as a wire mesh, may provide desired characteristics. (For more complete discussion see Chapter 12.)

Lower Thermal Expansion. Although epoxy resins do have a comparatively low degree of shrinkage (< 2 per cent), it must be taken into consideration in parts requiring a high degree of dimensional accuracy. Volume change or shrinkage of epoxies is due to both the curing reaction and the cooling from the peak exotherm temperature. Fillers cannot affect the cure-induced shrinkage, but they do reduce volume change on cooling, by reducing over-all coefficient of thermal expansion.

Fillers themselves have lower thermal expansion coefficients than epoxy resins. For example, compared with an epoxy system with a coefficient of expansion of $28 \times 10^{-6}/°F$, coefficients of marble, alumina, steel and aluminum are 0.28, 3.8, 7, and $14 \times 10^{-6}/°F$, respectively. Mixing such fillers with the resin provides intermediate coefficients. Such results can be particularly useful in applications where the resin is used next to another material.

Thixotropic Characteristics. Where resins must be applied to a near-vertical surface, fillers can be added to substantially increase viscosity, eliminating run-off and sag. Large quantities (150 to 300 parts/100 resin) of such fillers as atomized aluminum, tabular aluminum oxide and black iron oxide are required to substantially reduce viscosity, yet still permit pouring of the resin; much lower quantities (5 to 30 phr) of fibrillar materials such as asbestos, silica and calcium carbonate are required.

Colloidal silica can also be used to thicken epoxies temporarily during application to a near-vertical surface. Because of their high surface area, the particles tend to link together to form short fibers, which may form a pseudo-gel structure. Movement by brushing or pouring breaks the structure.

Kaolinites are less effective thixotroping agents than colloidal silicas, but are also less expensive. Kaolinites are hydrated aluminum silicates with platelet structures.

Typical thixotropes are "Cab-o-sil" (Godfrey Cabot), "Santocel" (Monsanto), and the "Bentones" (National Lead). Two to five parts/hundred of resin are usually required.

Mechanical Properties. Tensile strength and elongation are usually lowered with granular filler addition. However, compressive modulus can be doubled by sufficient loading with alumina or iron oxide. Abrasion resistance is almost tripled by addition of about 15 per cent graphite; titanium dioxide, nylon and molybdenum disulfide are effective to a lesser degree.

The use of chopped or milled glass fiber fillers or reinforcements substantially improves impact strength, as well as tensile strength and modulus.

Epoxy Laminates

Because of the variables involved in formulating and fabricating laminates, no tabulation of physical properties of laminates can be considered definitive. Actually values given in this discussion are typical, and are only obtained when the laminate is properly fabricated. General laminating techniques are discussed in Chapter 7; specific procedures for different formulations are available from materials suppliers.

Epoxy laminates reinforced with glass cloth can provide the highest strengths of any low-pressure reinforced plastic material (with the exception of filament wound structures). Their strength-to-weight ratio (tensile strength/specific gravity) is comparable to that of the strongest heat-treated wrought aluminum alloy, and superior to other aluminum alloys; it is superior to most steels in this respect. However, this com-

TABLE 4.1. REDUCED MECHANICAL PROPERTIES OF GLASS CLOTH-EPOXY LAMINATES [a]

	Angle of Load (deg)	Fabric			
		181	112	143	120
Tensile Properties					
Ult. strength, 1000 psi	0	45	45	85	45
	90	42.4	40	10.2	43.7
	45	26.6	21.7	12.7	22.8
Stress at proportional limit, 1000 psi [b] initial	0	11.1	13.2	30.7	15.4
	90	9.6	14	4.6	15.2
secondary	0	23.7	36.5	58.1	42.9
	90	19.9	36.5	6.75	43.2
	45	3.6	3.3	3.25	3.3
Modulus of elasticity, 10^6 psi [b] initial	0	3.32	3.13	4.86	3.06
	90	3.21	2.92	2.1	3.01
secondary	0	2.88	2.3	4.58	2.2
	90	2.66	2.13	1.82	2.17
	45	2.2	1.61	1.78	1.68
Compressive Properties					
Ult. strength, 1000 psi	0	45	45	60	45
	90	38.2	42.5	26.3	43.6
Stress at proportional limit, 1000 psi	0	20.6	17.7	27.7	18.4
	90	17.9	14.9	6.1	16.9
Modulus of elasticity, 10^6 psi	0	3.28	3.18	5.12	3.25
	90	3.14	3.1	2.08	2.85
Flexural Properties					
Modulus of rupture, 1000 psi	0	65	65	110	65
	90	57	58.4	21.7	62.4
Stress at proportional limit, 1000 psi	0	38.4	37.1	83.7	35.7
	90	35.2	30.6	11.4	38.1
Modulus of elasticity, 10^6 psi	0	3.2	3.2	5	3.2
	90	3.04	3.01	1.93	3.1
Shear Properties (edgewise)					
Ult. strength, 1000 psi		14	11.2	7.86	11.8
Stress at proportional limit, 1000 psi		1.8	1.65	1.63	1.65
Modulus of rigidity, 1000 psi		810	550	590	580

[a] All specimens parallel laminated; see text for derivation of reduced values; resins meeting MIL-R-9300.
[b] Secondary values show effect of prestressing.
Source: ANC 17 Handbook, "Plastics for Flight Vehicles."

parison is only on a strength-to-weight ratio basis. Disregarding weight, reinforced epoxies are not as strong on a unit area basis. Tensile strengths of the most widely used 181 cloth laminates are typically about 40 to 60 thousand psi.

One of the most important strength characteristics to remember in designing with reinforced plastics is the dependence of strength on the direction of reinforcement, as discussed in Chapter 3. Table 4.1 shows *reduced* mechanical properties for epoxy laminates with various types of glass cloth reinforcements. These values are generally allowable for design with any resin acceptable under specification MIL-R-9300. Effects of direction of loading are shown in values given for loading at 90 and 45 degrees to warp direction of the cloth reinforcement.

The reduced values shown in the table were obtained as follows: (1) typical strength values obtained by test were reduced to correspond with minimum *wet* values given in the specifications; and (2) since the specification gives no values for directions of loading other than the zero-degree-to-warp direction, values obtained by test in other directions were reduced by the same proportion as that found between average and specification values for zero degree warp. For example, if the specification value for tensile strength is 40,000 psi, and average value from test was found to be 50,000 psi, the value given in the table is 40,000 psi. Also for the same laminate, average test values for 90-degree tensile strength were multiplied by 0.80 to obtain the reduced values given in the table.

Both initial and secondary tensile values for modulus of elasticity and stress at proportional limit are given, indicating the effect of preloading. For design purposes, the average of the initial and secondary moduli is recommended.

Table 4.2 shows typical values obtainable with 181 glass cloth/epoxy with a "Volan" A finish. Values are for oven-cured specimens and property ranges are wide in an attempt to be all-inclusive. Room-temperature curing of laminates, as is sometimes necessary, usually results in somewhat lower mechanical strengths, and substantially lower heat resistance. Table 4.3 compares properties of a typical epoxy-181-Volan A laminate cured both at room temperature and postcured. Note the substantially lower flexural strength of the room-temperature cured specimen at 125°F. The 2 hours in boiling water tends to advance the cure of the resin, but flexural strength is still substantially below that of the oven-cured specimen.

Heat resistance of epoxy laminates is dependent on the resin, the cure, and the hardener used. Figure 4.2 shows strength *vs.* temperature for a

TABLE 4.2. TYPICAL PROPERTIES OF GLASS CLOTH-REINFORCED EPOXY LAMINATES

	ASTM	181 Volan A Cloth, ⅛-in. Laminate
Mechanical Properties		
Ult. tensile strength, 1000 psi	D638	40-65
Tensile modulus of elasticity, 10^6 psi	D638	3.04-4.5
Ult. flexural strength, 1000 psi	D790	50-100
Flexural modulus of elasticity, 10^6 psi	D790	2-3.7
Compressive strength, 1000 psi	D695	45-52
Izod impact strength, ft-lb/in. notch	D256	11-18
Hardness (Rockwell)	D785	M102-112
Physical Properties		
Specific gravity	D792	1.6-1.85
Coefficient of thermal expansion, 10^{-6}/°F	D325	8.8
Thermal conductivity, Btu/hr/sq ft/°F/in.	C177	2.3-2.4
Water absorption (24 hr), %	D570	0.02-0.07

conventional epoxy laminate cured with a high-temperature curing agent. Figure 4.3 shows flexural strength *vs.* temperature for three high-temperature epoxy laminate systems and a formulation based on the new peracetic acid-derived diepoxides.

Flexibilized epoxy resins can be used in laminates as well as castings, to improve impact resistance. The increase in elasticity or resilience of such systems is reflected in lower strengths and moduli. Table 4.4 shows effects of different polysulfide contents on mechanical properties of a laminate.

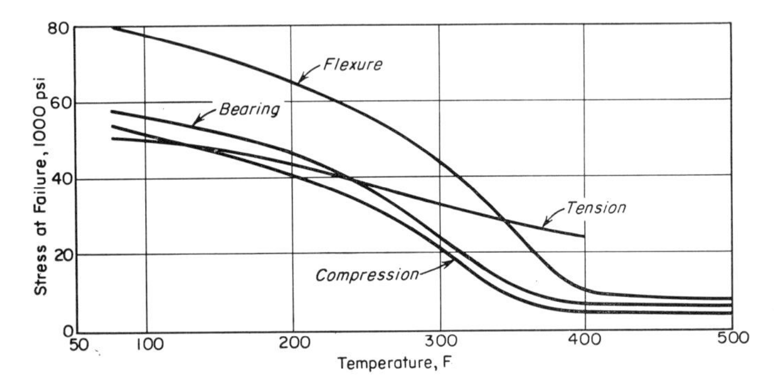

Figure 4.2. Effect of temperature on strength of laminate with conventional epoxy resin cured with high temperature curing agent. (*Military Handbook 17*)

TABLE 4.3. EFFECT OF OVEN CURE ON GLASS-EPOXY LAMINATES [a]

Mechanical Properties	Cured at Room Temp.	Postcured 8 hr at 320°F
Tensile strength, psi	36,100	40,700
Tensile modulus, psi	2.03×10^6	2.35×10^6
Compressive strength (edgewise), psi	38,100	43,000
Compressive modulus (edgewise), psi	2.94×10^6	2.83×10^6
Flexural strength, psi	52,500	61,800
Flexural modulus, psi	2.51×10^6	3.25×10^6
Flexural strength at 125°F, psi	7,600	46,600
Flexural modulus at 125°F, psi	0.38×10^6	2.37×10^6
Flexural strength (after 2 hr in 212°F water), psi	46,200	57,400
Flexural modulus (after 2 hr in 212°F water), psi	2.29×10^6	2.79×10^6
Izod impact strength, ft-lb/in. notch	12.4	10.4

[a] 181 Volan A Cloth; 12 ply, ⅛ in. thick laminate.
Source: Lee and Neville.[2]

Long-Time Loading. Although plastics tools are designed for prototype and short-run applications, in some cases they are used long enough for time effects to be noticeable. Reinforced epoxies are sensitive to duration

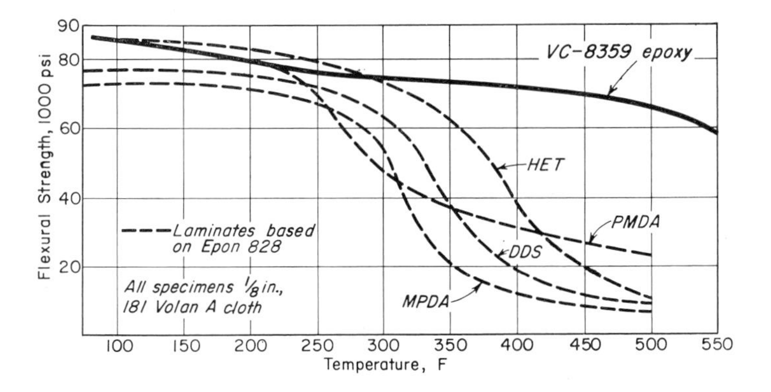

Figure 4.3. Effect of temperature on flexural strength of laminates made with the new diepoxide based resin (VC8359). Compared with that of laminates made with conventional epoxy and four different curing systems. (*Brunswick-Balk-Colander Co.*)

of loading, though these effects vary and definitive data are not available. The following discussion is intended to indicate the type and general magnitude of the effects of various long-time loading conditions.

Under fatigue conditions (cyclic stressing) reinforced plastics do not

TABLE 4.4. EFFECTS OF POLYSULFIDE FLEXIBILIZER ON MECHANICAL PROPERTIES OF GLASS-EPOXY LAMINATES [a]

Properties	Polysulfide (phr)						
	0	16.7	20	25	33.3	50	100
Compressive strength (edgewise), 10^3 psi	35	35	33	31	30	27	17
Flexural strength, 10^3 psi	65	63	61	60	59	35	10
Flexural strength (after 2 hr in 212°F water), 10^3 psi	38	37	32	31	30	20	15
Flexural modulus, 10^6 psi	3.1	3.0	2.9	2.8	2.6	2.1	1.3
Flexural modulus (after 2 hr in 212°F water), 10^6 psi	2.6	2.5	2.5	2.4	2.4	1.7	0.6
Izod impact strength, ft-lb/in. notch	11	11	12	12	14	15	16

[a] Resins: epoxy molecular weight 350 to 400.
polysulfide, molecular weight 1,000.
Curing agent: Tridimethylaminomethyl phenol at 10 phr.
Reinforcement: 181 Volan A Cloth, 12 plies.
Cure cycle: Pressed 30 to 60 min. at 248°F.
Source: Lee and Neville.[2]

appear to reach an endurance limit. Figure 4.4 shows SN curves for notched and unnotched epoxy laminates compared with polyester laminates. Curves are plotted as number of cycles to failure *vs.* amplitude of

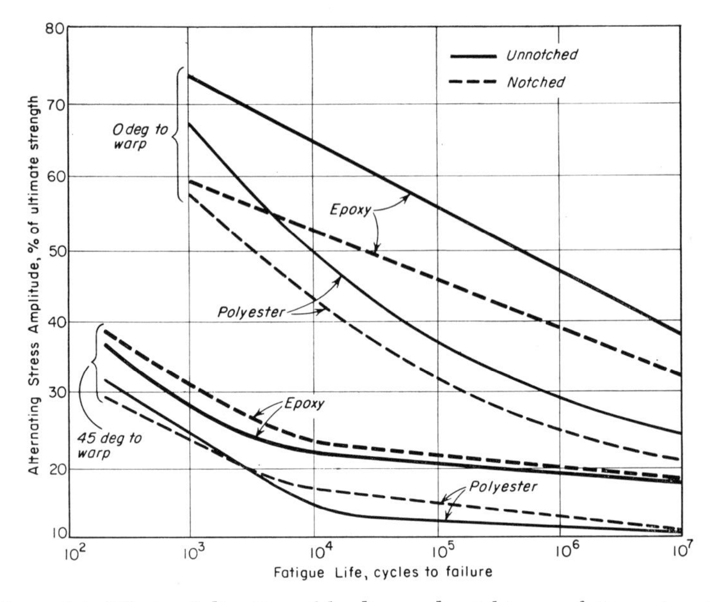

Figure 4.4. Effects of direction of loading and notching on fatigue strength of epoxy and polyester laminates. (*Military Handbook 17*)

alternating axial stress, expressed as a percentage of ultimate tensile stress. Zero mean stress was used, and stress was applied at 900 cycles/minute.

In specimens tested parallel to warp out to 10 million cycles, no clear-cut endurance limit is reached. In tests carried out at 45 degrees to warp, the "knees" in the curves indicate that endurance limits may have been reached.

The higher fatigue strength of epoxies, as compared with polyesters, under completely reversed alternating stresses, is to be expected since at

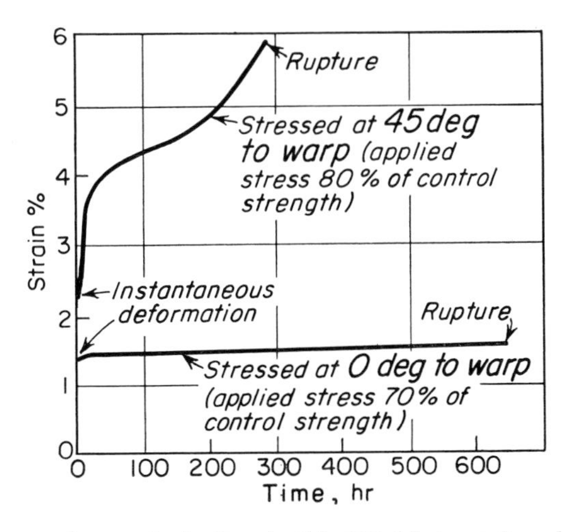

Figure 4.5. Creep under tensile loading in this 181 fabric-reinforced epoxy laminate is substantially higher in the 45 deg-to-warp direction than in the 0 deg direction. (*Military Handbook 17*)

zero mean stress both tensile and compressive strength of the material influence fatigue strength. Compressive strengths of epoxy laminates are about the same as tensile strengths, whereas compressive strengths of polyesters are usually substantially lower than tensile strengths.

Under flexural loading conditions fatigue strengths at 10 million cycles have been found to be about 20 to 30 per cent of short-time flexural strengths.

Although tensile creep of fabric-reinforced laminates appears to be negligible both parallel and perpendicular to warp, tensile loading at 45 degrees to warp direction results in substantial creep. Figure 4.5 compares creep-rupture of a 181 fabric-epoxy laminate when loaded at 0 and 45 degrees to warp.

Epoxy Castings

In cast form epoxies are used both for tool surfaces and for mass casting. Compared with cast phenolics, epoxies provide superior toughness, lower shrinkage, and optimum adhesion to metallic and nonmetallic inserts and/or core materials.

On the other hand, they are substantially more expensive, and the exotherm must be carefully controlled. If too high an internal temperature is reached (exotherm temperatures may reach as high as 300 to 400°F), some of the more volatile components may boil, causing voids as well as surface imperfections. Also, the effect of this exotherm on over-all dimensional shrinkage must be calculated.

At one time exotherm limited the size of epoxy castings drastically. However, today, through the use of such controlling ingredients as less reactive hardeners, fillers which can provide greater heat capacity, and/or better thermal dissipating characteristics, castings as large as 1500 to 2000 lb can be cast successfully in one pour. Such massive castings are usually not recommended. An alternate approach is to pour in stages, allowing each stage to generate and dissipate its exotherm before pouring the subsequent stage.

Table 4.5 shows typical properties of cast epoxy compositions. Flexibilized castings offer particular benefits in such applications as matched

TABLE 4.5 TYPICAL PROPERTIES OF EPOXY CASTINGS

	ASTM	Rigid [a]	Resilient [b]
Mechanical Properties			
Ult. tensile strength, 1000 psi	D638	8-11	4-8.6
Tensile modulus of elasticity, 10^5 psi	D638	3.8-4.6	—
Ult. flexural strength, 1000 psi	D790	14-20	8.2-15.2
Flexural modulus of elasticity, 10^5 psi	D790	4-4.5	1.4-3.0
Compressive strength, 1000 psi	D695	19-33	3-20
Izod impact strength, ft-lb/in. notch	D256	0.4-1.5	0.5-7.0
Hardness (Rockwell)	D785	M75-110	(50-75) [c]
Physical Properties			
Specific gravity	D792	1.11-1.23	1.0-1.25
Coefficient of thermal expansion, 10^{-6}/°F	D696	25-36	28-68
Thermal conductivity, Btu/hr/sq ft/°F/in.	C177	1.2-9.6	1.2
Water absorption (24 hr), %	D570	0.01-0.5	0.4-1.0
Heat distortion temp. (264 psi), °F	D648	150-360	105-220

[a] Range covers values obtainable with recommended postcures.
[b] Range covers common types using polysulfide or polyamide flexibilizers.
[c] Barcol hardness.

tooling for sheet metal forming since the resilience of the material eliminates the need for allowance for metal thickness.

The resilient formulations can be varied widely to provide different combinations of hardness and flexibility. For example, in the epoxy-polyamide systems, a 35:65 ratio of Versamid to epoxy provides high hardness and rigidity; a 70:30 ratio of Versamid to epoxy provides an extremely flexible material. Use of polyamide curing flexibilizers also provides benefits in reducing exotherm, since they react more slowly with the epoxy. This also provides longer pot lives, but on the other hand, slower cures. (At 300°F polyamide-epoxy blends cure more rapidly than conventional amine-cured epoxies.)

Pressure Casting. Although pressure casting itself is not new, a relatively recent and highly successful development has been the metal-and/or glass fiber-reinforced epoxy systems for pressure casting. The system is termed "Epoxy-Alloy" by Union Carbide Plastics Co. The process makes use of a high-temperature epoxy resin filled with steel, aluminum or glass fibers, cast under pressures ranging from 50 to 300 psi, depending on the composition.

In conjunction with the casting, a metal-fiber flocked face is recommended for critical tools. The three systems initially evaluated by Carbide were: (1) an epoxy pressure-casting reinforced with steel fibers and surfaced with an epoxy/steel-fiber flocked face coat; (2) An epoxy pressure-casting reinforced with glass fiber and surfaced with an epoxy/steel-fiber-flocked face coat; and (3) An epoxy pressure-casting reinforced with aluminum fibers and surfaced with an epoxy/aluminum fiber-flocked face coat. The last is primarily designed for uses requiring high thermal productivity, such as heated matched molds, etc.

Although the technique is not widely used at present, the following discussion is lengthy because of the high promise the materials and technique offer.

Typical properties of three systems are shown in Table 4.6 compared with those of an unfilled epoxy. The metal-fiber filled materials have excellent machinability and, when steel fiber is used, are magnetic. The filled compositions have good pot life, yet when metal fibers are used, exotherm is substantially reduced by the increased thermal capacity and conductivity of the fibers.

According to Mazzucchelli,[3] mechanical properties are improved by use of longer fibers, while homogeneity and handling improve as fiber length decreases. For mass casting, 0.75 to 2-in. fibers appear to offer the optimum balance. Short 0.25-in. fibers are used for flocking the face coat;

TABLE 4.6. TYPICAL PROPERTIES OF PRESSURE-CAST FIBER–REINFORCED EPOXY RESINS [a]

Properties	ASTM	Type of Fiber			
		None	Steel	Glass [b]	Aluminum
Specific gravity	D792	1.15	2.25	1.55	1.8
Flexural properties	D790				
Ult. strength, 1000 psi		17.5	11-16	16-29	8.5-13.5
Tang. proportional limit, 1000 psi		11.0	6.5-8.3	12-25	5.3-7.5
Modulus of elasticity, 10^6 psi		0.5	0.8-1.6	1.4-1.8	0.9-1.9
Compressive properties	D695				
Ult. strength, 1000 psi		33.5	12.5-28.5	21-29	12-21
Tang. proportional limit, 1000 psi		11.0	6.5-18.5	14-20	7.5-12
Modulus of elasticity, 10^6 psi		0.4	0.4-0.8	1.2-1.8	0.6-0.9
Ult. strength at 200°F, 1000 psi		–	7.7-22.5	16-22	8.9-14
Heat distortion temp. (264 psi), °F	D648	275	>400	>400	>400
Rockwell hardness	D785	M114	M72-82	M103-111	M56-81
Izod impact strength, ft-lb/in. notch	D256	0.4	0.8-1.6	11	0.7-1.6
Coefficient of thermal expansion, 10^{-6}/°F	D696	88	43	–	55
Thermal conductivity, Btu/hr/sq ft/°F/in.	c	2.0	19-30	5	51-131
Max. recommended service temp., °F	–	–	350	350	350
Water absorption (24 hr, 2 x ⅛ in. disk), %	–	0.16	0.30	0.40	0.35

[a] Properties measured perpendicular to casting pressure.
[b] With steel fiber face coat.
[c] Modified Ingen-Hausz method, described in "Practical Physics," by Marsh, White, *et al.*, New York, McGraw-Hill Book Co., Inc., 1955.
Source: Mazzucchelli.[3]

these do not appear to degrade properties seriously. Tables 4.7 and 4.8 indicate the effect of altering length of steel and aluminum fibers on physical properties.

Use of metal fiber reinforcement permits the casting of large masses of epoxy without the sacrifice in strength or toughness which may occur when using only high filler content to reduce exotherm. Fiber reinforcement reduces peak exotherms and concomitant high shrinkage and internal strains. Satisfactory fiber-reinforced pressure castings have been made as large as 81 x 51 x 28 in., weighing 3500 lb. Shrinkage varies from zero to 0.003 in./inch.

Although the process is still relatively new, data are available on effects of altering a number of materials and process variables. Table 4.9 shows properties obtained by using different resin systems (note that the reinforcement is continuous fiber). The room-temperature-curing epoxy

Table 4.7. Effect of Fiber Length on Properties of Steel Fiber-Reinforced Pressure-Cast Epoxy Resins [a]

Properties	ASTM	Length of Grade 1 Steel Fiber			
		Continuous	2-In.	¾-In.	¼-In.
Fiber content, % by weight		57	58	62	58
Flexural properties	D790				
Ult. strentgh, 1000 psi		15.6	11.7	10.9	16.1
Proportional limit, 1000 psi		8.4	6.6	6.2	12.4
Modulus of elasticity, 10^6 psi		1.5	1.0	0.9	1.5
Compressive properties	D695				
Ult. strength, 1000 psi		22.5	12.7	10.8	19.6
Proportional limit, 1000 psi		13.4	6.7	4.9	13.6
Modulus of elasticity, 10^6 psi		0.35	0.73	0.65	0.83
Ult. strength at 200°F, 1000 psi		15	7.8	7.4	15.2
Izod impact strength, ft-lb/in. notch	D256	1.3	1.6	1.6	0.9
Thermal conductivity, Btu/hr/sq ft/°F/in.	—	26	22	—	22

[a] Cast at 300 psi.
Source: Mazzucchelli.[3]

Table 4.8. Effect of Fiber Length on Properties of Aluminum Fiber-Reinforced Pressure-Cast Epoxy Resins [a]

Properties	ASTM	Fiber Length (Med. Grade)				
		Continuous		¾-In.		⅛-In.
		5056HS	Soft Temp.	Alloy 3003S	5056HS	5056HS
Fiber content, % by weight		29	46	46	26	35
Aluminum powder content, % weight		17	16	16	22	19
Flexural properties	D790					
Ult. strength, 1000 psi		11.4	13.5	8.8	11.2	10.7
Proportional limit, 1000 psi		7.8	7.5	5.3	7.6	7.6
Modulus of elasticity, 10^6 psi		1.2	1.9	0.9	1.1	1.2
Compressive properties	D695					
Ult. strength, 1000 psi		23.9	20.4	12.5	19.6	21.0
Proportional limit, 1000 psi		13.6	8.9	7.5	10.4	11.8
Modulus of elasticity, 10^6 psi		1.44	0.59	0.77	0.83	0.92
Ult. strength at 200°F, 1000 psi		18.9	14.1	9.0	13.0	14.2
Izod impact strength, ft-lb/in. notch	D256	1.4	1.6	1.0	0.8	0.7
Thermal conductivity, Btu/hr/sq ft/°F/in.	b	51.5	132	94.4	28.6	—

[a] Heat-resistant epoxy; cast at 300 psi.
[b] Modified Ingen-Hausz Method as described in "Practical Physics," by Marsh, White, *et al.*, New York, McGraw-Hill Book Co., Inc., 1955.
Source: Mazzucchelli.[3]

TABLE 4.9. EFFECT OF RESIN TYPE ON PROPERTIES OF FIBER-REINFORECD PRESSURE-CAST MATERIALS [a]

	ASTM	Heat-Resistant Epoxy (Oven-Cured)		Resin Type: Room-Temp.-Cured Epoxy	Resin Type: Rigid Polyester
		Continuous Steel Fiber Grade			
		Grade 3	Grade 1	Grade 3	Grade 1
Fiber content, % by weight		40	57	44	55
Iron powder content, % by weight		15	—	15	—
Flexural properties	D790				
Ult. strength, 1000 psi		18.5	15.6	21.1	9.5
Proportional limit, 1000 psi		13.4	8.4	11.6	7.7
Modulus of elasticity, 10^6 psi		1.8	1.5	2.2	1.3
Compressive properties	D695				
Ult. strength, 1000 psi		21.8	22.5	29.6	35.6
Proportional limit, 1000 psi		12.7	13.4	18.2	17.4
Ult. strength at 200°F, 1000 psi		17.2	—	9.9	—
Izod impact strength, ft-lb/in. notch	D256	1.6	1.3	2.3	1.6

[a] Heat-resistant epoxy cast at 300 psi.
Source: Mazzucchelli.[3]

resin system (with slightly higher fiber content) gives slightly higher strength at room temperature, but lower strength at 200°F. The room-temperature system is also poorer in resistance to abrasion and creep, although it is still better than systems using only powder fillers. Of course, the long pot life of the heat-resistant epoxy system is desirable for fabrication of large castings.

The type of metal fiber used is one of the most significant variables in such materials. Commercial metal fibers available are essentially shavings obtained by the conventional metal wool process. They have a polygonal cross section, generally triangular, with sharp edges. They are graded according to size with cross sections varying from 0.0018 to 0.0080 in. The effect of variation in fiber coarseness is shown in Table 4.10. Generally, increasing coarseness of steel fiber from grade 0 to 3 improves physical properties slightly. Grade 1 has been most frequently used for making dies because it can provide lower porosity, better resin and fiber distribution and improved homogeneity.

Possibilities of improvement in properties by use of other types of metal fibers and wire are shown in Table 4.11. Note particularly the improved mechanical properties obtained with annealed wire, and the impact

TABLE 4.10. EFFECT OF FIBER GRADE ON PROPERTIES OF STEEL-FIBER PRESSURE-CAST EPOXY RESINS [a]

	ASTM	Steel Fiber Grade		
		Grade 0	Grade 1	Grade 3
Fiber content, % by weight		41	40	44
Iron powder filler, % by weight		17	17	16
Flexural properties	D790			
Ult. strength, 1000 psi		17.5	22.9	21.1
Proportional limit, 1000 psi		13.1	12.1	11.6
Modulus of elasticity, 10^6 psi		1.7	2.1	2.2
Compressive properties	D695			
Ult. strength, 1000 psi		20.8	25.7	29.6
Proportional limit, 1000 psi		10.0	13.4	18.2
Ult. strength at 200°F, 1000 psi		5.5	12.9	9.9
Izod impact strength, ft-lb/in. notch	D256	0.9	1.1	2.3
Thermal conductivity, Btu/hr/sq ft/°F/in.		24	20	25

[a] Room-temperature-curing epoxy system; cast at 300 psi.
Source: Mazzucchelli.[3]

TABLE 4.11. PROPERTIES OBTAINABLE WITH EXPERIMENTAL STEEL FIBERS IN PRESSURE-CAST EPOXY RESINS [a]

	ASTM	Fiber Form			
		Continuous			Short
		Treatment or Condition			
		Silver-Plated, Grade 1 [b]	Annealed, Grade 1	Drawn, Annealed Wire [c]	¼-In. (0.002 x 0.015 in.) [d]
Fiber content, % by weight		59	65	63	63
Flexural properties	D790				
Ult. strength, 1000 psi		16.8	13.1	17	12.1
Proportional limit, 1000 psi		9.5	7.2	12.7	6.7
Modulus of elasticity, 10^6 psi		1.6	1.9	2.0	1.5
Compressive properties	D695				
Ult. strength, 1000 psi	—	—	22.6	30.4	18.8
Proportional limit, 1000 psi		—	13.3	13.7	8.2
Modulus of elasticity, 10^6 psi		—	0.70	0.38	1.0
Izod impact strength, ft-lb/in. notch	D256	1.8	1.0	4.4	2.4
Thermal conductivity, Btu/hr/sq ft/°F/in.	e	152	—	26	—

[a] Heat-resistant epoxy system cast at 300 psi.
[b] 33 per cent silver, 62 per cent steel.
[c] Wire 0.006 in. diameter.
[d] Experimental fibers.
[e] Modified Ingen-Hausz Method as described in "Practical Physics," by Marsh, White, *et al.* New York, McGraw Hill Book Co., Inc., 1955.
Source: Mazzucchelli.[3]

strength of the ¼-in. fiber materials, which is substantially improved over that of other ¼-in. fiber reinforced compositions. Bronze, stainless steel, and degreased steel fibers have shown no particular property benefit.

Metal fiber preforms and densified mats of 0.25 to 0.33-in. steel fibers are available experimentally in densities varying up to 30 per cent fiber content by volume, and in a range of thicknesses from $\frac{1}{16}$ in. upward to over 1 inch. They can be cut to shape with a band saw and tailored over patterns. Infiltration by liquid resin systems takes place readily by capillary action. Sintered or metallurgically bonded low-carbon steel mats can also be obtained in various densities. High porosity mats (up to 20 per cent steel by volume) can be shaped by hand and absorb resin quickly. One of the major problems in use of mats is their rigidity and poor "drape."

In comparing unsintered and sintered mats impregnated with 33 per cent by weight of heat-resistant epoxy resin, unsintered composites offer flexural strengths of 11,900 psi and a flex modulus of about 880,000 psi compared with flexural strengths of 23,000 psi, and modulus of 1 million psi for sintered reinforcements. Thermal conductivity of the sintered composition is also higher, i.e., 51 versus 24 Btu/hr/sq ft/°F/in.

Table 4.12 shows the improvements obtained in properties by postcuring the cast mass. Extended postcure typically upgrades compressive

TABLE 4.12. EFFECT OF POSTCURE ON PROPERTIES OF STEEL FIBER-REINFORCED PRESSURE-CAST EPOXY RESINS [a]

	ASTM	Room-Temp.-Cured [b]	Postcured 20 Hr, 300°F
Flexural properties	D790		
Ult. strength, 1000 psi		18.7	16.4
Proportional limit, 1000 psi		11.5	7.3
Modulus of elasticity, 10^6 psi		1.1	1.6
Compressive properties	D695		
Ult. strength, 1000 psi		20.1	28.8
Proportional limit, 1000 psi		13.5	18.5
Modulus of elasticity, 10^6 psi		1.09	0.50
Tensile properties	D638		
Ult. strength, 1000 psi		7.8	6.4
Proportional limit, 1000 psi		6.2	5.1
Modulus of elasticity, 10^6 psi		1.4	1.5
Elongation, %		0.59	0.48
Izod impact strength, ft-lb/in. notch	D256	1.1	1.2

[a] Heat-resistant epoxy system; cast at 300 psi; reinforced with 60 per cent by weight of Grade 1 continuous steel fiber.
[b] Casting experienced peak exotherm of 320°F.
Source: Mazzucchelli.[3]

strength at some sacrifice in tensile strength. Tests indicate that adequate cure is obtained when both the surface and interior of the casting is held for 2 hr at 300°F.

Both metal-filled types can be heated by either induction or direct low-voltage resistance heating. Experiments indicate that about 10 watts/lb capacity are required to heat an insulated cast to 300°F for 2 hr. Such a technique offers a possibility of curing large casts without an oven. It would also avoid heat transfer problems through the thickness of the cast.

The most significant results of early studies of the material, according to Mazzucchelli,[3] were those obtained on experimental terminal-box draw dies, fabricated from various materials. The terminal box was drawn from a 7½-in. diameter blank of 20-gage cold-rolled steel to form a 4-in.-square motor terminal box over on 0.109-in. draw radius to a depth of 1-¾ to 2-⅜ inches. A steel blank holder was used with the die mounted, inverted, in a 93-ton fast-acting crank press for operation at speeds of 600 to 1000 stampings/hr.

The depth of draw and speed of operation were such that the stampings reached temperatures of over 140°F, and the dies 115 to 144 F, as measured 0.050 in. from the draw-radius surface at the corners. This combined effect accentuated wear and breakdown of the plastics, permitting rapid comparative evaluation of the different die materials used. Each die was fitted carefully for metal thickness clearance for the most accurate comparison. Durable dies were tested to 1000 stampings; poorer dies were stopped after 200 stampings.

Table 4.13 summarizes the data for the most important die compositions tested, listing the materials in ascending order from the poorest to best. The room-temperature epoxy-surfaced iron-core dies, representing present commercial draw-die materials, show up very poorly in this test, with considerable wear and galling.

Use of glass fiber-reinforced pressure-cast heat-resistant epoxy rather than polyester improved performance, but there was considerable ridging of the die surface and uneven wear, resulting from abrasion of the glass fibers. Application of an iron-powder face coat to the glass-epoxy improved surface wear, but presented process problems in that the face coat was found difficult to apply and hold to the die contours.

A heat-resistant epoxy casting reinforced with glass fibers and surfaced with a steel-fiber flocked face coat gave very uniform wear and dimensional stability, with easy application of the face coat. Performance was considered excellent.

The steel fiber-reinforced heat-resistant epoxy die with the steel fiber-flocked face coat also gave excellent results in regard to uniformity of

TABLE 4.13. WEAR TEST COMPARISON, TERMINAL BOX DRAW DIES

Die Composition [a]	No. of Stampings	Draw Radius Change from Initial 0.109 in., in.		Remarks
		Corners with 2⅝-in. Draw Depth	Straight Edge With 1¾-in. Draw Depth	
Pressure-cast–PG	200	Eroded	+0.06	Severe erosion and breakdowns
Surface-cast–RTESC	200	+0.12	+0.04	Very severe galling and erosion
Pressure-cast–EG-GF	500	+0.15	+0.03	Uneven wear, ridging due to abrasion
Pressure-cast–EG-IPF	1000	+0.3	+0.01	Slight uneven wear and ridging; face coat difficult to apply
Pressure-cast–EG-SF	1000	+0.08	+0.01	Uniform wear; face coat easy to apply
Pressure-cast–ES	1000	+0.08	+0.03	Uniform wear
Kirksite alloy	1000	0	−0.01	Uniform wear; least erosion, but creeps, and metal flake builds up on radius

[a] PG = Polyester-glass.
RTESC = Room-temperature epoxy surface coat on iron core.
EG-GF = Heat-resistant epoxy-glass, with glass flock face.
EG-IPF = Heat-resistant epoxy-glass, iron powder-filled face.
EG-SF = Heat-resistant epoxy-glass, steel flock face.
ES = Heat-resistant epoxy-steel fiber, with steel flock face.

Source: Mazzucchelli.[3]

wear, while retention of dimensions was even better than that of a Kirksite alloy die. This material also has advantages of homogeneity and machinability over the system using the glass fiber-reinforced core; but the latter has certain process advantages, such as simpler equipment and greater applicability to large, complex dies.

Kirksite dies showed less wearability but greater dimensional change than the metal fiber-reinforced dies tested. The draw radius of the Kirksite die actually decreased due to buildup of metal moving from the die surface. Although the metal-fiber reinforced dies tested show a great improvement in erosion resistance over previous plastic materials, they are not quite as good as Kirksite dies, due probably to their lower hardness. This was reflected in better looking stampings (disregarding dimensions) obtained with the Kirksite die.

In regard to material selection, i.e., when to use metal fiber and when to use glass fiber in the composition, definitive conclusions cannot be drawn. The decision will be based on specific requirements and availability of equipment. Table 4.14 compares the two materials in both processing characteristics and general property benefits.

TABLE 4.14. COMPARISON OF STEEL VS. GLASS-FIBER REINFORCEMENT IN PRESSURE-CAST EPOXY RESINS [a]

	Epoxy-Glass, Steel Flock Face	Epoxy-Steel, Steel Flock Face
Fabrication		
Build-up: depth of cast ratio	0.25-0.50	3-4 [b]
Face coat	Greater care [b]	Easy
Presaturation of fibers	Yes	No
Casting pressure, psi	50-100	200-300
Fiber movement	Yes	No
Complex dies	Easy	More difficult
Properties		
Homogeneity	No	Yes
Machinability	Poor [b]	Excellent
Die modification	More difficult	Easy
Thermal conductivity	Poor	Excellent
Mechanical properties	Very good	Adequate
Die performance	Good	Good

[a] High-temperature epoxy systems.
[b] Condition improved with use of densified metal-fiber mats when available.

Pastes and Putties

Epoxy pastes or putties are essentially casting or laminating resins which have been highly filled with any of a variety of fillers or reinforcements to provide distinctive end properties. Pastes can be used both for patching and repair of metal or plastics tools, or for fabricating the entire tool.

Probably the most common types of epoxy pastes use steel, iron or aluminum powder fillers. High filler loading (60 to 80 per cent metal powder) provides the cured material with metal-like qualities. Other types of fillers include inorganic materials and milled glass fibers.

Typical properties of cured pastes are shown in Table 4.15. Actually a wide range of properties is obtainable by altering filler type and content.

TABLE 4.15. TYPICAL PROPERTIES OBTAINABLE IN SOME COMMERCIAL EPOXY PASTES OR PATCHING COMPOUNDS [a]

Properties	ASTM	Steel Powder-Filled	Aluminum Powder-Filled	Self-Lubricating [b]	Resilient [c]
Ult. tensile strength, 1000 psi	D638	5.3-10	6-9	8	4-5
Tensile modulus of elasticity, 10^6 psi	D638	0.85	—	—	—
Ult. compressive strength, 1000 psi	D695	16.7-18	18-30	16	9.3
Ult. flexural strength, 1000 psi	D790	13	11-19	11	—
Izod impact strength, ft-lb/in. notch	D256	1	0.8-1.1	0.8	1.1-40
Hardness (Rockwell)	D785	F93	F93-97	F93	(65-76)[d]
Coefficient of thermal expansion, 10^{-6}/°F	D696	14	25	—	35
Thermal conductivity, Btu/hr/sq ft/°F/in.	—	3.6	6.7-7.8	—	—
Specific gravity	D792	2.5-2.8	1.3-1.8	1.8	1.2

[a] Because of extremely wide range of properties obtainable by altering resin systems and fillers, these ranges only indicate some typical properties obtainable; both conventional and high-temperature epoxies are used; materials are available as liquids or trowelable pastes.
[b] Specific fillers not given by manufacturers, but such fillers as graphite or molybdenum disulfide may be used.
[c] General properties obtainable either with polysulfide or polyamide flexibilizers.
[d] Shore D scale.

Where needed, thermal expansion characteristics of pastes can be altered to closely approximate those of other materials. The materials provide excellent adhesion to a variety of materials, will not attack metals, and are available with excellent machinability.

Epoxy Foams

Several types of epoxy foams have been produced, all of the rigid type. They are newer than the phenolic foams, and higher materials costs plus the more intricate handling required have somewhat retarded their acceptance for lightweight core constructions. At present, phenolics are more widely used for such applications, although epoxies offer somewhat superior mechanical strengths. Epoxy foams are supplied as (1) prefoamed boards or planks, (2) pack-in-place systems, or (3) foam-in-place systems. General characteristics of the three types are shown in Table 4.16.

A fourth type of foam is the syntactic foam, in which phenolic or urea microballoons form the cells of the foam, and are bound together with a liquid epoxy resin.

A relatively new development (although not used in tooling) is the

TABLE 4.16. GENERAL CHARACTERISTICS OF EPOXY FOAMS

	Prefoamed [a]	Pack-In-Place [b]	Foam-In-Place [c]
Heat required (for expansion or cure), °F	None	77-350	77-225
Cell structure	Closed and partially open	Closed and partially open	Open and closed
Density, lb/cu ft	5-38	15-25	5-8
Compressive strength, psi	50-6000	600-3000	80-110
Flexural strength, psi	200-4500	500-2500	—
Coefficient of thermal expansion, 10^{-6}/°F	8.3	8.3	—
Thermal conductivity, Btu/hr/sq ft/°F/in.	<0.65	0.24-0.8	0.24
Heat stability, °F	To 500	To 600	To 300
Dielectric strength, v/mil	350	300	65
Dielectric constant	2.0-7.0	2.5-7.0	1.55
Dissipation factor	0.005-0.030	<0.030	—

[a] Cubes: 15 in.; planks: 1 x 6 x 1-to-2 ft; sheets: 12 x 12 x 1, 2, or 3 in.; rods: 12 in. long, 1, 2 or 3 in. diameter.
[b] One- and two-component systems, similar in consistency to damp sand.
[c] One-, two-, and three-component systems.
Source: "Plastics Engineering Handbook."

use of epoxy resin with polystyrene expandable beads. The liquid epoxy and the beads are mixed together along with appropriate epoxy curing agents, and poured into the void to be filled. The exotherm generated by the curing epoxy expands the polystyrene beads. The finished foam consists of expanded polystyrene beads, bonded together with the epoxy resin. During foaming sufficient epoxy is forced to the surfaces to form an impermeable surface coating.

Since definite published data on formulation and processing of epoxy foams are lacking, materials suppliers should be consulted for information on these materials. Additional discussion of foams can be found in Chapter 10.

REFERENCES

1. Delmonte, J., "Control of Physical Properties," paper presented at 25th Anniversary Meeting, American Society of Tool Engineers, Mar. 1957.
2. Lee, H., and Neville, K., "Epoxy Resins, Their Applications and Technology," New York, McGraw-Hill Book Co., Inc., 1957.
3. Mazzucchelli, A. P., "New Fiber-Reinforced Epoxy Compositions," paper presented before the Society of The Plastics Industry, Inc., Reinforced Plastics Div., 13th Annual Conference, Feb. 1958.
4. *MIL-Handbook-17,* "Plastics for Flight Vehicles, Part I, Reinforced Plastics."
5. Riley, M. W., "Low Pressure Reinforced Plastics," *Materials in Design Engineering* (Feb. 1960).
6. Skeist, I., "Epoxy Resins," New York, Reinhold Publishing Corp., 1958.

5. *Other Tooling Plastics: Phenolics, Polyesters, Flexible Mold Materials*

In addition to epoxy resins, phenolics and polyesters are the two plastics materials used to any extent for tooling. Ethyl cellulose, a thermoplastic that must be melted and cast hot, appeared promising at one time for tools requiring a high degree of resilience, such as drop-hammer punches. However, the resilient or flexibilized epoxies have for the most part replaced the material.

The other material discussed here is the relatively new RTV (room-temperature vulcanizing) silicone rubber, which has been receiving increasing interest recently as a flexible mold material. Although not truly a plastic, it does fit into a discussion of plastics tooling. Liquid polysulfide polymers ("Thiokols"), plastisols, latices, and neoprene have been used for flexible mold materials for casting models and prototype parts in the past. However, the RTV overcomes many of their limitations and offers substantial benefits.

PHENOLIC RESINS

In plastics tooling, phenolic resins are used either as (1) castings, both for cast tool surfaces and mass castings, or (2) foams for lightweight cores.

Phenolic resins are one of the oldest plastics materials. Often erroneously called "bakelite" (Bakelite is a registered trade name of Union Carbide Plastics Co., used to designate not only phenolics, but several of their plastics materials), phenolics are also one of the most varied and versatile plastics produced. Their major attributes include low cost, heat resistance, good mechanical strength, rigidity, good electrical insulating properties and good chemical resistance. On the other hand, in the cast form they are relatively brittle; they usually require oven-curing and usually cure with a relatively high degree of shrinkage, though shrinkage can be substantially reduced by use of proper fillers.

Industrially, phenolics are most widely used as compression- and transfer-molding compounds, coatings and varnishes, and high-pressure laminates (industrial thermosetting laminates). The condensation reaction by which they cure requires that high laminating pressures be used in order to obtain good adhesion to reinforcements. Low-pressure laminating that has been done with phenolics has been mostly with preimpregnated materials, which are usually costly and require higher pressures than commonly used for tooling.

Consequently, castings and foams are the primary forms in which phenolics are used in tooling. In this form, they provide a low cost mass of material that serves either as 1) a hard, rigid (but somewhat brittle) tool surface, or 2) a light weight core or backing material.

Chemistry

Most commercial phenolics are formed by the condensation of a phenol (characterized by the presence of an hydroxyl group attached to a benzene ring) with formaldehyde to form a thermosetting resin. According to Anderson,[1] the curing mechanism by which phenol alcohols condense to resins is divided into three stages. The A-stage resin, or *resol,* is the initial condensation product of phenol and formaldehyde. Phenolic casting resins are usually liquid solutions of resol which can be cured with heat.

The B-stage resin, or *resitol,* is the second stage of condensation, and since cross-linkage has not proceeded very far, the material is still somewhat thermoplastic and can be softened by heat (e.g., molding compounds and prepregs). The final C-stage resin, or *resite,* is the fully cured material in which there is a high degree of cross-linking. These three stages are not clearly defined, but blend gradually into one another.

Accelerators and Cures

Casting resins are usually relatively stable, and require acidic accelerators to speed up cross-linking to the degree required for practical cure cycles. For example, a standard formulation may maintain initial viscosity for a period of about 3 months at room temperature. For longer periods of time, resins should be stored at temperatures of about 30°F.

Cure can be extremely rapid if proper accelerators are used. For example, with sufficient accelerator content, the mix will cure in a few minutes. However, to provide strain-free castings, room-temperature cures should be extended to at least 24 hr. But room-temperature-cured castings should only be used for noncritical applications, as optimum physical properties are not developed without oven-curing.

For developing optimum properties, the resin should first be brought to room temperature (about 70°F) from storage temperature. After addition of accelerator, and pouring, castings should be permitted to precure for 16 hr at room temperature. For postcure, oven time and temperature depend on type of resin system and size of casting. For example, for one commercial formulation, 12 to 16 hr at 200°F is recommended for castings of 100 lb or less; 16 to 24 hr at 200°F for castings of more than 100 lb.

Handling Precautions

The accelerators used with phenolic resins are acidic; consequently, mixing containers and equipment must be of acid-resistant materials. Also, metallic inserts or core materials to be used in contact with the phenolic in the tool must be coated to protect them from attack. Epoxy coatings can provide the desired protection.

Castings

One of the most important advantages of phenolics is low cost. Casting resins cost about 45 to 70¢/lb (2.3 to 3.4¢/cu in.). In addition to the low materials cost, the casting process is relatively inexpensive, resulting in a low-cost final tool.

Table 5.1 gives typical physical properties of both unfilled and mineral- and asbestos-filled phenolic castings. The asbestos filler helps prevent chipping and reduces shrinkage characteristics. Types of fillers are limited by the acidic nature of accelerators used with phenolic resins.

Superior heat resistance of phenolics has been one of the major claims for the material for tools in the past. However, in *cast form,* ASTM heat-distortion temperatures (264 psi) are only about 200 to 260°F, and maximum recommended continuous service temperatures for some grades are only about 300°F. The difference between these values and those of some of the newer improved metal fiber-reinforced heat-resistant epoxy formulations is marginal. Also, the condensation curing reaction of phenolics usually results in a degree of moisture within a casting. Continued exposure to heat can result in blistering.

Consequently, the place to use cast phenolics in tooling is where the low cost casting process is desired, where hardness and rigidity is needed, and where the brittleness of the material will not cause major problems.

TABLE 5.1. TYPICAL PROPERTIES OF CAST PHENOLICS

	ASTM	Mechanical and Chemical	Mineral-Filled	Asbestos-Filled
Specific gravity	D792	1.26-1.30	1.68-1.70	1.70
Tensile strength, 1000 psi	D638	4-9	4-9	3-6
Tensile modulus of elasticity, 10^5 psi	D638	5-7	—	18-19
Flexural strength, 1000 psi	D790	8-14	9-12	4-8
Flexural modulus of elasticity, 10^5 psi	D790	3-7	—	19
Compressive strength, 1000 psi	D695	10-20	29-34	10-13
Izod impact strength, ft-lb/in. notch	D256	0.2-0.4	0.3-0.5	—
Hardness (Rockwell)	D785	M70-110	M85-120	R110
Heat distortion temp. (264 psi), °F	D648	165-260	150-175	—
Water absorption (24 hr), %	D570	0.2-0.4	0.12-0.36	—
Coefficient of thermal expansion, 10^5/°F	D696	3.3-4.4	4.2	1.8

Source: Data adapted from: Materials Selector Issue, 1959-60 Reference Issue, Materials in Design Engineering; "Modern Plastics Encyclopedia," 1960; and Gould.[4]

Foams

Phenolic foams are of two major types: (1) foam-in-place, and (2) syntactic foams. Foam-in-place phenolics are usually supplied as three-component systems, consisting of resin, accelerator and a foaming agent. The materials should be brought to a temperature of about 77°F before mixing; warming the mold slightly may be necessary to obtain best results. The ingredients should then be intimately mixed. With some types, beating the mix with a propeller type agitator for 5 sec is recommended. The mixture is then poured rapidly into the foaming container. Lower density materials will foam in 7 to 8 sec; higher density foams react more slowly. Catalyst concentration and temperature of ingredients can be varied to alter the speed of the foaming reaction.

Although the foams can be produced in any container, maintaining a slight back pressure on the solution during the exothermic reaction is advisable. A simple method of maintaining this pressure is to invert a container of the desired shape over the foaming pan. As the foam expands the weight of the container provides sufficient back pressure for the foam to fill the container uniformly.

Densities of foam-in-place phenolic foams may range from a low of about 2 lb/cu ft (about 40 psi compressive strength) to as high as 22 lb/cu ft (about 1125 psi compressive strength). More information will be found in the discussion of core materials in Chapter 10.

Syntactic foams, as described in Chapter 4, consist of phenolic or urea microballoons bonded with liquid resin. The binding resin can be phenolic as well as epoxy. After mixing with the microballoons, the material is of putty-like consistency and can be troweled into place. It then hardens to form a lightweight foam of closed cell structure.

POLYESTER RESINS

Polyester resins were the first low-pressure laminating resins suitable for wet lay-up with glass cloth to conform to compound curvatures. Consequently, they were one of the early tooling plastics. They wet glass cloth easily, cure rapidly either at room temperature or with heat, and provide high-strength, low-cost tools with relatively good thermal stability.

Their major problem is shrinkage (0.06 to 0.08 in./in.), making close tolerance tooling difficult. Also, after gelation the resins set rapidly, much of the shrinkage taking place after the resin has set, often resulting in distortion or warpage of the finished tool. Epoxy resins have replaced polyesters almost completely in tooling. Epoxies have substantially lower shrinkage (0.001 to 0.004 in./in.), and the bulk of the shrinkage takes place while the resin is in the liquid state, resulting in a minimum of strains in the cured part.

The major benefits polyesters offer are their low cost of 30 to 35¢/lb (1.5 to 1.75¢/cu in.), and their excellent processing and curing characteristics in reinforced plastics fabrication. Strength, durability, thermal stability and chemical resistance are also good. These attributes have resulted in a remarkable expansion in the use of polyesters for an extremely wide variety of consumer and industrial products, including boats, furniture, and transportation and communications equipment. In fact, virtually all the products commonly (and somewhat erroneously) referred to today as being made of "fiberglas" are reinforced polyester. But in plastics tooling, where materials costs are a very small part of the over-all cost of the tool, for the most part polyesters have been replaced by epoxies.

On the other hand, it is not necessary to make a better tool than is needed. There are still many tools which do not require the accuracy and stability of epoxies. For these noncritical tools polyester resins can provide economies both in materials costs and processing.

Chemistry

The term "polyester" means literally "many esters," and thus includes an extremely large group of materials. As commonly used in the plastics industry, the term refers to those products of the reaction between dibasic acids, such as phthalic anhydride or maleic anhydride, and polyols, such as propylene glycol. This reaction product is an unsaturated polyester, which is then dissolved in a monomer such as styrene (most commonly used), diallyl phthalate, vinyl toluene or triallyl cyanurate, which serves as a cross-linking agent. An inhibitor is then added to prevent premature gelation of the resin.

Cure of the liquid resin is initiated by addition of a catalyst, usually an organic peroxide or hydroperoxide. Activators or accelerators are often used to promote the cross-linking reaction at room temperature. Cure takes place in two stages: the first stage is the formation of a soft gel, which may take place in a few minutes or several hours, depending on temperature and on the inhibitor-catalyst-promoter balance. Immediately after gelation, cure is rapidly propagated with evolution of considerable heat.

There are innumerable types of polyester resins available. There are rigid, semirigid and flexible types; heat-resistant types; flame-resistant types; chemical-resistant types; etc. For the most part, styrene-containing low-cost general-purpose polyesters have been the most widely used for tooling.

Recently developed resins which may prove to be of significance in tooling are the isophthalic polyesters (made by reacting isophthalic acid rather than other dibasic acids such as phthalic anhydride, with a glycol and adding the monomeric cross-linking agent). The materials are still relatively new, and data are incomplete, but they do appear to offer substantial improvements in wet strength, impact strength, and certain processing characteristics.

Laminates

As mentioned before, properties of reinforced plastic laminates are dependent on so many variables that a definitive listing is impractical. Table 5.2 lists reduced mechanical properties of polyester laminates (derivation of reduced values is given in the section on epoxy laminates in Chapter 4). These values are generally allowable for design with any polyester resin acceptable under MIL-R-7575. Table 5.3 lists typical mechanical properties obtainable with conventional polyesters reinforced

TABLE 5.2. REDUCED MECHANICAL PROPERTIES OF POLYESTER LAMINATES [a]

	Type of Fabric					
	Angle of Load (deg from warp)	181	128	143	120	Mat
Tensile Properties						
Ult. strength, 1000 psi	0	38	38	75	38	18
	90	35.1	29.2	8.95	35.7	18
	45	17.8	17.2	11.7	17.9	18
Str. at prop. limit, 1000 psi [b]						
Initial	0	5.45	4.9	–	9.5	2.8
	90	5.2	4.75	2.2	5.0	2.8
Secondary	0	22.6	29.1	51.5	28.6	8.1
	90	19.4	24.46	7.1	20.1	8.1
	45	2.85	3.94	3.3	2.9	8.1
Modulus of elasticity, 10^6 psi [b]						
Initial	0	2.62	2.82	–	2.88	1.46
	90	2.49	2.17	1.6	2.79	1.46
Secondary	0	2.34	2.47	5.39	2.56	1.18
	90	2.15	1.7	0.42	2.41	1.18
	45	1.57	1.41	1.57	1.76	1.18
Compressive Properties						
Ult. strength, 1000 psi	0	30	21	45	30	18
	90	31.6	20.9	19	26.1	18
Str. at prop. limit, 1000 psi	0	19.6	21	45	30	18
	90	19.8	20.9	19	21.1	18
Modulus of elasticity, 10^6 psi	0	2.94	2.9	4.91	2.78	1.61 [c]
	90	2.82	2.22	1.51	2.71	1.37 [d]
Flexural Properties						
Modulus of rupture, 1000 psi	0	45	39	78	45	22
	90	40.9	33.1	15.1	35.7	22
Str. at prop. limit, 1000 psi	0	27.8	21.7	69.5	25.4	11.9
	90	24	16.5	4.7	19.5	11.9
Modulus of elasticity, 10^6 psi	0	2.5	2.5	4.5	2.5	1.2
	90	2.35	1.94	1.36	2.43	1.2
Shear Properties (edgewise)						
Ult. strength, 1000 psi	–	9.18	8.92	7.44	9.23	9.2
Str. at prop. limit, 1000 psi	–	1.42	1.45	1.63	1.42	3.1
Modulus of rigidity, 1000 psi	–	570	510	550	640	610

[a] All specimens parallel laminated; see text for derivation of reduced values; MIL-R-7575 resins.
[b] Secondary values show effect of prestressing. [c] Initial. [d] Secondary.
Source: "Military Handbook 17."

with cloth and mat. Property ranges are wide in an attempt to be all-inclusive.

Mechanical strengths obtainable in laminates are somewhat lower than those obtainable in epoxy laminates; water absorption is substantially higher.

TABLE 5.3. TYPICAL PROPERTIES OF POLYESTER LAMINATES
(Styrene or DAP Type Polyester)

		Reinforcement	
		Cloth (12 ply, 181)	Mat (202)
Mechanical Properties	ASTM		
Ult. tensile strength, 1000 psi	D638	25-55	8-25
Tensile modulus of elasticity, 10^6 psi	D630	2.2-3.1	0.9-1.7
Ult. elongation, %	D630	1.7-1.8	1.2-2.3
Ult. flexural strength, 1000 psi	D790	33-75	20-40
Flexural modulus of elasticity, 10^6 psi	D790	2.0-3.8	1.0-2.5
Compressive strength, 1000 psi	D695	27.7-45	14.5-31
Compressive modulus of elasticity, 10^6 psi	D695	—	—
Izod impact strength, ft-lb/in. notch	D256	10-20	7-15
Hardness			
Rockwell	D785	M100-120	M80-120
Barcol	—	55-72	40-55
Physical Properties			
Specific gravity	D792	1.6-2.0	1.15-2.2
Coefficient of thermal expansion, 10^{-5}/°F	D325	—	1.0-1.4
Water absorption (24 hr), %	D570	0.2-0.8	0.2-2.0

Castings

The high shrinkage of polyesters has precluded their broad use as castings for tooling applications, although a pressure casting technique was used somewhat successfully for a number of years. Essentially it is the same technique as pressure-casting of epoxy, except that glass fibers have usually been used. The process consists of casting the chopped fiber-reinforced polyester under pressures of about 20 to 40 psi against the back of a prepared laminated tool surface. Maintenance of continual pressure during cure of the material compensates for shrinkage, and fills any voids as they occur.

Compared with epoxy pressure casts, polyester casts have greater creep and poorer abrasion resistance.

RTV SILICONE RUBBER

The benefits of flexible mold materials for molding cast plastics models or prototypes and parts are obvious, i.e., ability to remove easily parts with re-entrant angles and to re-use such molds. A variety of flexible mold materials such as plastisol, latex, neoprene and polysulfide liquid polymers (Thiokols), have been used successfully.

Recently developed RTV (room-temperature vulcanizing) silicone rubber is creating increasing interest because it offers substantial benefits over all of these materials. According to Dutt,[3] RTV offers the following benefits in epoxy model reproduction:

1. *Low Shrinkage.* Compounds cure at room temperature and have a shrinkage factor of less than 0.2 per cent.

2. *Elimination of Parting Agent.* Silicone rubber molds have built-in release agent. No parting agent is required for even the most complex parts, including undercuts. This results in faster fabrication of models and elimination of mold build-up.

3. *Excellent Surface Detail.* The RTV conforms to intricate detail on surfaces of master molds, reproducing the detail exactly with a high finish on the final cast epoxy part.

4. *Variability of Pot Life.* By using different catalysts, pot life of the RTV can be adjusted from as short as 3 min. to as long as 4 hr at room temperature. Cure time will vary from 10 min. to 24 hr.

5. *Versatility of Viscosity.* Compounds are available in viscosities ranging from that of an easily pourable liquid for casting, to a thick paste which can be applied with a spatula. To make models of heavy difficult-to-move objects, the liquid can be painted on the surface to pick up the detail; the paste can then be spread over the liquid RTV to add body and firmness to the mold.

6. *Heat Resistance.* RTV compounds are resistant to temperatures as high as 600°F (*vs.* about 240 to 260°F for neoprene and polysulfide), permitting oven cure of epoxy resins in the mold.

7. *Re-usability.* The toughness of the compound permits re-use of the mold for a number of parts, depending on complexity of the part being formed and the resin system being cast.

Properties and Behavior

Table 5.4 lists typical properties of several RTV silicone rubber compounds. As shown, the compounds have sufficient toughness and strength

TABLE 5.4. TYPICAL PROPERTIES OF RTV SILICONE RUBBER

	Type			
	RTV Liquids			RTV Paste
	Shore Durometer Hardness (ASTM, D676)			
	A50 [a]	A55 [b]	A60 [c]	A60 [d]
Fabricating Properties				
Consistency	Easily poured	Pourable	Pourable	Stiff paste
Viscosity, cps	30,000	45,000	70,000	12×10^5
Typical cure time (firm), hr				
"Silicure" L-24 [e]	24-48	24-48	48-72	24-48
"Thermolite"-12	16-24	8-12	16-24	1-4
Linear shrinkage, %	0.2	0.2	0.2	0.2
Physical Properties				
Specific gravity	1.30	1.37	1.45	1.45
Tensile strength (D412), psi	450	550	650	750
Elongation (D412), %	140	120	110	160
Tear strength (D624, die B), lb/in.	25	25	50	50
Peel strength (D429), lb/in [f]	—	4.0	4.5 [g]	6.5 [g]
Electrical Properties [h]				
Volume resistivity (D257), 10^{13} ohm-cm	1.5		1.5	
Dielectric strength (D149), v/mil	500		500	
Dielectric constant (D150, 60 cps)	4.0		4.0	
Power factor (D150, 60 cps), %	1-2		1-2	
Chemical Resistance [i] (D471)				
ASTM No. 1 Oil (70 hr, 300°F)				
Hardness Change, Shore A units	−15		−5	−10
Tensile strength change, %	−30		−10	−35
Elongation change, %	0		0	−30
Weight change, %	+25		+2.0	+1.2
Volume change, %	+5.1		+3.8	+3.0
"Skydrol" 500 (70 hr, 80°F)				
Hardness Change, Shore A units	−4		−3	−5
Tensile strength change, %	−10		−5	−15
Elongation change, %	0		−30	−20
Weight change, %	2.9		+2.1	+2.8
Volume change, %	3.6		+3.0	+4.2
5% NaCl-Distilled Water (70 hr, 80°F)				
Hardness Change, Shore A units	0		−5	−5
Tensile strength change, %	0		0	−5
Elongation change, %	0		0	−20
Weight change, %	0		+1	+1.0
Volume change, %	0		+1	+2.2
JP-4 Jet Fuel (70 hr, 80°F)				
Hardness Change, Shore A units	—		−7	−15
Tensile strength change, %	—		−25	−50
Elongation change, %	—		−65	−45
Weight change, %	—		+55	+80
Volume change, %	—		+110	+180

[a] G.E. grade: RTV-20. [b] G.E. grade: RTV-40. [c] G.E. grade: RTV-60. [d] G.E. grade: RTV-90.
[e] Nuodex Products Co.; Silicure T-773 can provide 30-min. cure for the A55 durometer stock.
[f] Bonded to primed 18-8 stainless steel. [g] Rubber failed.
[h] RTV tests made at 77°F, 50% RH on 0.08-in. ASTM slabs cured 72 hr at 80°F.
[i] RTV compounds: cold-pressed ASTM sheets cured with 1% Silicure L24 for 144 hr at 80°F.

to be used repeatedly. The life of the flexible mold depends primarily on the type of hardener used to cure the epoxy casting. Some strong amine curing agents may limit mold life to 6 to 8 parts; other types of hardeners permit production of 30 to 40 parts from the same mold.

In addition to changing curing agents, other techniques are available for modifying pot life and curing times. For example when the concentration of one type of metallic salt curing agent ("Thermolite" 12) is

(*General Electric Co.*)

Figure 5.1. Detail obtainable with RTV silicone rubber is shown by this wire inserting fixture used in the manufacture of magnetic memory storage units.

reduced from 1.0 to 0.1 per cent, pot life of one compound is increased from 30 min. to 3 to 4 hr. Such a decrease in amount of curing agent does not alter cured properties.

Heat (up to 200°F) may also be used to reduce cure time. If heat is applied to RTV after it is poured, the shorter cure time does not affect pot life. If thick-section silicone molds are used for curing high temperature epoxy resins, the molds should be conditioned by heating in 50°F increments for 4 hr or more, starting at 250°F up to the maximum curing temperature.

Viscosity of RTV compounds can be reducel by mixing with a silicone fluid. General Electric indicates that use of their RTV 20 can reduce the initial 30,000 cps viscosity to 19,000 cps with 5 phr (parts per hundred parts RTV) of fluid, and to 11,000 cps with 10 phr. Twenty phr of fluid reduced viscosity of G.E. RTV-90 from 1,200,000 cps to 200,000 cps.

Such reductions in viscosity are said to result with little sacrifice in physical properties of the cured rubber.

A pressure-casting technique for use with RTV rubber molds detailed by Dutt at an SPE-ASTME Meeting, results in exceptional reproduction of detail where intricate complex shapes are to be formed. The RTV silicone rubber mold is poured and cured. The epoxy is mixed and cast in the RTV mold. The filled mold is then placed in a paint-spray pressure chamber which serves as an autoclave. A pressure of 50 to 80 psi is built up within the chamber, and is held until the epoxy has had a chance to thoroughly cure, after which the mold is removed and the part stripped.

The "autoclave" pressure is evidently sufficient to cast the material completely void free. Although what actually happens to entrapped air is not fully understood, Lubin of Grumman suggests that the pressure forces it into solution with components of the epoxy system. Dutt demonstrated the fidelity of reproduction by such a procedure by playing a 33 rpm phonograph record pressure cast of epoxy in an RTV mold.

REFERENCES

1. Anderson, R. S., "Phenolics," in "Modern Plastics Encyclopedia," New York, Breskin Publishing Co., 1959.
2. Berridge, C. A., and Treat, R. Jr., "Silicone Rubbers That Cure at Room Temperature," *Materials in Design Engineering* (Jan. 1960).
3. Dutt, D. E., and Treat, R. Jr., "Simplified and More Accurate Model Reproduction with RTV Silicone Rubber," paper presented before Annual Meeting, American Society of Tool Engineers, April 1959.
4. Gould, D. F., "Phenolic Resins," New York, Reinhold Publishing Corp., 1959.
5. Riley, M. W., "Low Pressure Reinforced Plastics," *Materials in Design Engineering* (Feb. 1960).

6. *Reinforcements for Tooling Plastics: Fibers—Honeycomb—Metal and Ceramic Coatings*

Grouped here are (1) fibrous materials, both glass and metal, which reinforce plastics materials in a manner analogous to that of steel in reinforced concrete, (2) honeycomb materials that are being used in some types of tooling to provide low cost, high strength-weight characteristics by replacing a number of layers of reinforcement in a laminate, and (3) metal or ceramic coatings used not so much as structural reinforcement, but to provide a tool surface with such characteristics as wear or abrasion resistance, good thermal conduction and dissipation, or heat resistance, or combinations of these properties.

FIBROUS GLASS

By far the most widely used reinforcing material for tooling plastics (and reinforced plastics in general) is fibrous glass, or fiberglass (the term "fiberglass" now appears generically in dictionaries as describing a material made of glass fibers; *note:* the word itself does not imply the presence of any resin).

Plastics resins themselves are relatively low strength, low modulus materials. Fibrous reinforcements contribute the primary structural strength. Consequently, the strength characteristics of a laminate are highly dependent on the direction or orientation of the glass fibers within the resin matrix and the degree of adhesion between the resin and the glass. To provide a wide choice in directional characteristics, as well as wide variation in such properties as drape, bulk, surface smoothness, glass content, and adaptability to various fabricating techniques, fibrous glass is available in a variety of forms, e.g., chopped strand or roving, fabrics in a variety of weaves, and nonwoven mats in a variety of weights.

Most of the glass reinforcements used in tooling plastics are either (1) chopped strand for reinforcement of bulk castings or putties, (2) woven fabrics for high-strength laminates, or (3) nonwoven mats for laminates where maximum strength is not as important as the need for isotropic strength characteristics. Combinations of these reinforcing materials are also used.

Considering the number of types of glass reinforcements available, only a relative few are being put to use in tools. For example, probably two or three basic weaves account for virtually all of the cloth used in tooling laminates. Such an approach greatly simplifies matters; however, with the substantial improvements which have come about in (1) techniques of designing plastics tools, and (2) understanding how they behave (e.g., more accurate stress analysis), there is no reason why the versatility available in glass reinforcements cannot be put to better use. This can be done by analyzing the stress configurations which will be set up in the tool in service, and accurately prepositioning glass fibers in the tool to carry the required loads most effectively. This, of course, is an ideal which can seldom be completely realized. But a better understanding of the various types of glass reinforcements available can be of great help in more nearly approaching this ideal.

A textile is a highly complex structure, whose properties depend on both the base fiber and the textile form in which it is used. For example, some of the variables which determine the performance of a textile are (1) the type and nature of the base fiber, e.g., cross-sectional shape and size and whether it is a monofilament (continuous filament) or multifilament (staple fiber) yarn, (2) the number of fibers and degree of twist in the yarn, and (3) type of weave, including such variables as number of ends (yarns) in warp (longitudinal) and fill (transverse) directions, degree of crimp in the yarns as they cross under and over other yarns, etc. In short, a textile can be visualized as a complex structure consisting of innumerable tiny beams (filaments), each of which is loaded in a highly complex way to provide a cumulative set of engineering properties.

The Fibers

Most fibrous glass used in tooling laminates is "E" glass, made from a lime-alumina borosilicate glass that is relatively soda-free. Of the three basic production methods (steam or air blowing, flame blowing, mechanically pulling) mechanical pulling is usually used to produce filaments for plastics reinforcements, since most reinforcing cloths are made from filament rather than staple yarns.

In the mechanical drawing process, glass ingredients are melted in a gas-fired furnace. The molten glass is fed into a "bushing" which contains a number of orifices through which the glass flows. Continuous filaments are then drawn from the molten glass stream. During the early stages of cooling the stream is attenuated into filaments by being pulled at very high speeds—usually ranging from 5000 to 10,000 fpm—from the bushing. Resulting filaments have diameters of 0.00020 to 0.00075 in., depending on pulling speed, orifice size, molten glass temperature, and other variables.

For efficient production, a number of filaments are pulled simultaneously from several orifices in the bushing. These filaments (usually about 204) are collected into a bundle, called a *strand,* at a gathering device where a "size" is applied to the filament surfaces. The strand is then wound into a forming package called a "cake." From this cake, shippable forms of fibrous glass are produced.

The size, applied to the surface after formation of the filament, should not be confused with "finishes" applied after the fibrous glass is in the final textile form. Bare glass filaments are highly susceptible to abrasion; also, because of the high ratio of surface area to volume in filaments (1 lb of roving has about 880 sq ft of surface), the nature of its surface greatly affects properties of the filament. Consequently, the freshly-produced filament which is to be used in yarns and woven fabrics must be protected from abrasion caused by subsequent production steps such as spinning, winding and weaving. The size, applied at the gathering device, serves as surface protection and lubricating agent, and as a binder to hold the filaments together in the strand.

Unfortunately, sizes which provide the most effective lubrication for highly abrasive weaving operations do not provide good "priming" or coupling action between glass and resins used in laminating. Consequently, woven fabrics must be heat-cleaned to remove the lubricating size, and effective coupling agents or finishes must be applied by the glass supplier before the cloth is purchased for laminating. Finishes generally used are either of the chrome type, such as Volan A, or silanes; the choice is dictated by the type of service (wet or dry), strengths required, and cost considerations.

In the manufacture of some types of reinforcements, such as mats, rovings and chopped strands, the fibers are not subjected to rigorous abrasion. In the processing of such reinforcements, initial sizes can be selected which provide lubrication, strand-binding, and resin-glass coupling. The elimination of the heat cleaning and finishing operation generally reduces the cost of such reinforcements.

Forms Available

The following are the various types of reinforcements available. Though some are not widely used now for tooling they may provide the answer to some specialized tooling problem which the most common types cannot solve effectively.

Rovings. Rovings consist of a number of strands (usually 60) gathered together from cake packages and wound on a tube to form a cylindrical package. Rovings have very little or no twist. They are used either to provide completely unidirectional strength characteristics, such as in filament winding, or are chopped into predetermined lengths for preform molding or spray molding.

Chopped Strand. Strands can be cut into short lengths (usually ½ to 2 in.) in a manner similar to chopped roving, for use in preform molding, spray molding or to make molding compounds. It is the least expensive form of fibrous glass reinforcement.

Milled Fibers. Continuous strands from basic forming cakes can be hammer-milled into small modules of filamented glass (nominal lengths: $\frac{1}{32}$ to ¼ in.). Largely used for filler reinforcement in casting resins and in resin adhesives, they provide greater body and dimensional stability.

Yarns. Either filaments or staple fibers (short strands of fiber) can be twisted into yarns on standard textile equipment from the basic forming package. Although primarily an intermediate form from which woven fabrics are made, yarns are used for making rod stock, and for some very high-strength unidirectionally reinforced shapes. A common form in which yarn is available is the warp beam, where many parallel yarns are wrapped on a mandrel. Though not widely used, it is a convenient form of handling a large number of yarns used for unidirectional reinforcement.

Nonwoven Mats. Glass mats are available both as reinforcing mats and as surfacing or overlay mats.

Reinforcing mats are made of either chopped strands or swirled continuous strands laid down in a random pattern. Strands are held together by resinous binders (bonded glass fabrics).

In laminates, mats provide relatively low strength levels, but strengths are isotropic. Mats are specified by weight (oz/sq yd). They are lower in cost than woven fabrics, but slightly more expensive than bulk chopped strands or rovings. Costs vary according to weight and bonding method.

Surfacing and overlay mats are both thin mats of staple monofilaments. They provide practically no mechanical reinforcement, but stabilize the surface resin coat and allow the use of a heavy layer of resin. They are usually used in conjunction with reinforcing mats or fabrics. They usually range in thickness from 0.010 to 0.030 in., and are bonded with resins that provide maximum water resistance. Unlike reinforcing mats, surface and overlay mats are made of filaments rather than strands.

The difference between surfacing and overlay mats lies in stiffness. Surfacing mats contain more binder resin, making them rather stiff. Consequently they are used primarily on flat or simple contoured parts. Overlay mats have a lesser amount of binder, so they are fluffy and extremely drapable. Although not as easy to handle as surfacing mats, overlay mats can be used on complex contours.

Woven Fabrics and Rovings. Woven fabrics and woven rovings provide the highest strength characteristics to laminates, though strengths are orthotropic. Fabrics are more expensive than mats.

Many kinds of fabrics and tapes are available. They vary in weight, thickness, style of weave, coarseness of yarn and fiber diameter. Although both continuous filament and staple yarns are used, the continuous type is most common because of its higher strength. Because yarns in woven fabrics have predetermined and reproducible directionality, a wide range of directional strength characteristics is obtainable by shifting alternating plies of cloth in a laminate.

Woven rovings are relatively new, but are highly promising, both from the standpoint of performance and cost. Fabrics are made by weaving bulky rovings rather than spun yarns. Resulting fabrics are thick, coarse, high strength, highly drapable, and lower in cost than yarn fabrics. (Rovings do not require heat cleaning and finishing, consequently initial size provides final finish, reducing final cost.)

Although a wide variety of weaves is available, the most common types include:

Plain Weave. Firmest and most stable of the industrial weaves, the plain weave consists of one warp end (lengthwise yarn) over and then under one filling pick (crosswise yarn). It affords fair porosity with minimum yarn slippage and ease of air removal in hand lay-up or molding. Strength is essentially the same in the 0 and 90° to warp directions.

Basket Weave. Less stable but more pliable than a plain weave, basket weave has two or more warp ends weaving as one end over and under two or more filling picks. It is flatter and stronger than an equivalent weight and count of plain weave.

Crowfoot Satin. More pliable than either a plain weave or a basket weave, crowfoot satin is particularly designed to conform closely to complex or compound curved surfaces. It is constructed with one warp end weaving over three and under one filling pick. It makes possible the weaving of higher counts than plain or basket weaves.

Long Shaft Satin. Most pliable of the weaves, long shaft satins conform readily to compound curves. Construction varies, but consists of one warp end weaving over at least four and under one filling pick (e.g., eight shaft satin has one warp end weaving over seven and under one filling pick). It is a closer weave, can be woven into the highest density construction, and produces laminates with high strength in both 0 and 90° to warp directions.

Unidirectional Weave. Adaptable from any of the basic textile weaves, unidirectional weaves have a greater number of relatively strong warp yarns and fewer and generally weaker filling yarns. They provide maximum strength in one direction, and high impact strength.

Leno Weave. Produced by interlocking two or more parallel warp ends, the leno weave is useful in reducing sleaziness in low-count openly woven fabrics. The mock-leno special weave is used in tooling to provide excellent mechanical bonding and increased thickness at a lower fabric cost. It is a variation on the plain weave. Two or more warp ends and two or more filling picks are closely spaced or bunched together, the closely spaced groups alternating with loosely spaced yarn. The resulting fabric has a rough texture, increased thickness and additional porosity.

Fabric Finishes

The purpose of the finish, applied to the woven fabric after removal of sizing, is to improve the bond between resin and glass. The exact mechanism by which this is accomplished is still not known. It may be by (1) providing a molecular link between the glass and the resin by primary chemical bonds, or (2) increasing coefficients of friction between the resin and glass surface, or (3) acting as a deformable layer capable of relaxing shear stresses at the glass-resin interface, or (4) providing a combination effect of these three.

For most tooling jobs, the finish need not be of concern to the toolmaker. Glass textile producers will supply fabrics incorporating finishes to suit particular needs. By far the most common finish for glass cloth is "Volan A," a chrome finish (methacrylate chromic chloride complex, neutralized with ammonia). It provides good bonds with either polyester or epoxy resins. It also provides reasonably good bonds with phenolics. It is chemically similar to the older finish #114.

The other commonly used family of glass fabric finishes is the silanes. They are used primarily to provide improved wet strength. Of these, "Garan," "A-172," "136" and "301" are used principally with polyester resins; "NOL 24," a silane finish developed by the Naval Ordnance Laboratory (reaction product of allyltrichlorosilane and resorcinol), can be used as a universal finish to provide good bonds with polyesters, epoxies, phenolics and silicones. "A-1100," an amino silane (hydrolysis product of γ-aminopropyltriethoxysilane) provides excellent bonds with epoxy and phenolic resins.

Textile Specification Terms

To anyone not a textile engineer, the language of textiles is a strange one. The purpose of this brief discussion is to explain some of the terms used by the textile supplier to describe his product. Fortunately for the tool engineer, textiles used for tooling are almost exclusively glass, and he need not worry about other textile systems.

Table 6.1 shows typical specifications for glass fabrics supplied by one company. That company indicates that probably 80 per cent of their sales for tooling consist of the 3 fabrics: 2-P122, 2-P146, and 2-P460. As can be seen specifications usually include:

1. *Style.* Numbered designations are usually proprietary and in many cases indicate the style of the weave. Designations may include the number of such standard styles, such as 181 (satin), 112 (plain), 120 (crowfoot), 128 (plain), or 143 (unidirectional-crowfoot), or variations of these developed by individual textile suppliers. Explanations of proprietary designations are obtainable from suppliers.
2. *Standard put-up, or yield.* This indicates average length of rolls, in yards.
3. *Width, weight and thickness.* These are expressed in inches, ounces per square yard, and mils.
4. *Type of weave.* This indicates plain, satin, leno, crowfoot, etc.
5. *Thread count.* The number of yarns in the warp (longitudinal) and filling (transverse) directions; e.g., 16 $\times$ 14 indicates 16 warp yarns and 14 filling yarns.
6. *Yarn Numbers, both for warp and fill.* A typical yarn number for either warp or fill might be shown on the specification as 150/4/2. The first group of digits (in this case "150") designates the weight of the

TABLE 6.1. TYPICAL GLASS FABRIC SPECIFICATIONS [a]

Proprietary Fabric Designation	Standard Width (in.)	Put Up, (avg. yds/ roll)	Weave	Yarn	Constr. W x F	Thick-ness [b] (mils)	Weight (oz/yd²)	Min. Breaking Strength [c] (lb)	
								W	F
1-P28	38,44,50	300	Plain	225	42x32	8	6.00	277	211
1-P43	38	200	Crow-foot	225	49x30	10	8.90	647	66
1-P62	38	175	Plain	225	28x16	16	12.20	616	352
1-P81	38,44,50, 60,72	125	Satin	225	57x54	10	8.90	376	356
1-P83	38	100	Satin	225	54x48	20	16.75	713	634
1-P91	50	300	Leno	225	20x10	7	1.62	88	44
2-P127	38,44,50, 60	100	Plain	150	18x18	10	5.85	216	216
2-P128	38,44,50	300	Plain	150	42x32	8	6.00	252	192
2-P138	38	250	Crow-foot	225	60x55	7	6.15	264	242
2-P141	38,44,50, 60,72	100	Plain	150	18x17	14	8.55	324	306
2-P145	38,44,50, 60	100	Plain	150	16x14	12	7.32	288	252
2-P146	38,44,50, 60	100	Plain	150	16x14	14	9.66	384	336
2-P147	38	125	Crow-foot	150	48x30	16	12.56	576	360
2-P161	38,44,50	100	Plain	150	16x14	17	11.05	432	378
2-P182	38,44,50	125	Satin	150	60x56	14.5	12.65	504	450
2-P224	38	250	Crow-foot	150	57x30	7	5.39	342	66
2-P482	38,44,50	100	Mock Leno	150	42x21	30	20.65	1008	504

[a] These data supplied by Coast Mfg & Supply Co. for their Trevarno Fabrics. Specifications from other suppliers differ primarily in proprietary designations.
[b] Values are given as a guide only and not as a specification. Values are determined by Randall-Stickney Gauge Fed. Spec. CCC-T-191B.
[c] Values are given as a guide only and not as a specification. Values are determined by the warp and fill construction times the minimum breaking strength of the yarns as outlined in MIL-Y-1140C. Test values generally are in excess of the above figures given for minimum strength.

yarn used, as determined by the glass yarn numbering system (number of 100 yd lengths/lb). In this case, the basic singles yarn yields 15,000 yards/lb. (Single yarns are the basic filament yarn or strand taken from the filament-forming bushing, and which is then plied to form weaving yarn.) The "/4/2" portion of the designation means that the yarn used for weaving the cloth was made by twisting 4 singles of 150's together, and then twisting or plying 2 of the resulting yarns to make an 8-ply yarn.

7. *Strength.* Minimum average breaking strength of fabrics (ASTM D39 for woven fabrics; D1117 for nonwovens) is also usually given in the specification, as pounds warp and pounds fill. Often the specification shows, for example, 450 × 410 lb, indicating the breaking strength in warp direction is 450 lb; in filling direction it is 410 lb.

Selecting the Reinforcement

No definitive rules can be laid down by which the fabric can be chosen to use for each specific type of tool laminate. The following discussion summarizes results found most satisfactory by a variety of experienced tooling people. For specialized tooling requirements, the recommendation of either an experienced tooling plastic formulator or a reliable textile producer should be obtained. Ultimately, with a thorough knowledge of the fabrics, the resins and fabrication technology, you will be able to solve your own problems.

The initial problem is one of contradiction between cost and performance. On the one hand, from the economy standpoint, requirements call for (1) heavy fabrics which provide thick laminates with few plies, resulting in minimum lay-up time and lowest materials cost per pound, (2) open fabrics which provide economy in cloth, high resin pick-up and good rigidity-to-weight ratio due to low bulk of glass, and (3) drapability, which must be extremely high for tool designs involving intricate, sharp configurations.

On the other hand, from the performance standpoint, highest strengths result in laminates made with thin glass cloths, at least on the outer stressed surface. Over-all strength decreases as fabric thickness increases. The diminishing strength effect of increased thickness is greatest in compression. Impact strength varies directly with thickness, thicker fabrics providing generally higher impact strengths.

An important benefit of plastics for tooling is the control obtainable over directionality of strength by controlling the direction of reinforcing fibers, and by using combinations of different types of reinforcing textiles. However, such combinations must be carefully controlled. Warping occurs when an unbalanced combination permits unequal stresses to develop in service. Where different types of cloth and mat are used to provide the proper balance of resistance to tensile, compressive and flexural loads, the differences in moduli and strengths of each form of reinforcement tend to cause warpage unless construction is such that strengths within the laminate are exactly balanced out.

In general, the following recommendations can be made:

1. Plain weave fabrics should be used for laminated components of tools requiring bidirectional strength characteristics, and ease of removal of air under low-pressure contact or bag laminating pressures.
2. Satin fabrics (eight-shaft satins have been found satisfactory in heavier fabrics) are used where bidirectional strength characteristics are required, but where higher strengths are needed than obtainable with plain weaves of comparable thickness. Such weaves provide these strength characteristics with a minimum of lay-up labor. Also they tend to reduce materials costs, since thicker fabrics cost less per pound, and reduce lay-up waste and rejections due to air entrapment. They also provide a smooth, decorative surface.
3. Unidirectional fabrics are used where loading stresses can be carefully analyzed, definitely established, and the material oriented to provide the desired directional strength. They are also used for reinforcement of local areas and for providing excessive strength at a minimum of weight. Unidirectional fabrics must be laminated to a specific pattern, consequently, fabrication costs are usually increased by the hand labor involved.

Where optimum smoothness and strength of a tool surface is required, the first two layers of glass cloth should generally be of a fine weave, not exceeding 7 to 8 mils in thickness. Subsequent layers can be substantially heavier.

Roving, random fibers and milled fibers are largely used for local reinforcing, such as in corners. Chopped fibers are commonly mixed with resin to form a "gunk" used for build-up.

FIBROUS METAL

The use of metal fiber reinforcements in plastics is relatively new. It is one of the most promising developments in plastics tooling. Because it is so new, its full potential has not been realized, nor are its technicalities fully understood. Results of work on pressure-cast epoxy tools, described elsewhere, indicate its potential. The most important benefits from the tooling standpoint are improvements in resistance to wear and abrasion, and improvements in heat capacity, conduction and dissipation, and in some cases, lower cost tools. Strengths of such reinforced materials are on the order of those obtainable in mat-reinforced laminates.

The status at present is as follows. The greatest success has been obtained with ½- to 1-in. aluminum fibers reinforcing high-temperature epoxy resins. Other types of fibers, such as copper and mild steel, have also been used. Molybdenum fibers (about $240/lb, as compared with prices for 100 lb or over of about $1.80 to $3.50/lb for aluminum, $2.45 to $2.65 for copper, and 95¢/lb for steel) have been found to provide excellent stability in areas of high wear.

Metal fibers can be economically applied by spraying against a gel coat surface layer of resin (spray guns are available for as little as $87); or fibers can be applied in bulk and impregnated with resin by pressure or vacuum; or, fibers can be preimpregnated with resin prior to loading into a pressure-casting mold. A variety of combinations have been tested, including aluminum fiber reinforced tool surfaces, backed with either steel or glass fiber-filled cast cores, or aluminum copper or steel fiber-reinforced surface with a variety of backing materials, including metal or plaster. Work to date with densified metal-fiber mats or sintered preforms has been limited.

The following section describes work done in metal fiber technology which holds definite promise for tooling.

The Fibers

Metal fibers available today are essentially shavings obtained by the conventional metal wool process; or they may be wires, filaments or turnings, which are chopped or milled to produce discrete fibers. The fibers, which can be made of either equal or random lengths, are then crimped or beaten to produce random three-dimensional kinks.

The fibers generally have polygonal cross sections, generally triangular, with sharp edges. Their cross section varies from 0.0018 to 0.0080 in. Fine fibers, less than 0.001 in. in diameter and 0.010 in. long have been used in forming felts and mats; still finer fibers are of interest, but are generally unavailable at present.

Present commercial steel and aluminum fibers have a relatively high bulk density and high spring-back characteristics. Data have been obtained by applying pressure to 1½ to 3 lb of fibers in an 8-in. diameter mold, and measuring fiber volume at different pressures. Resistance of the fibers to compression increases rapidly around 50 psi and at higher pressures increases at an increasing rate.

According to Mazzucchelli, of the commercial fibers tested, the 2-in. precompressed and randomized steel fibers provide the best practical compromise. Annealed steel fibers are so "dead" that they may present problems in resin distribution in direct casting systems unless presaturated with the resin system; however, annealed continuous aluminum fibers have been successfully used in making matched molds.

Felted Mats and Preforms

Mazzucchelli mentions densified mats of ¼ to ⅜ in. steel fibers in thicknesses from $\frac{1}{16}$ in. upward to over an inch, which can be cut to shape with a bandsaw and tailored over patterns. Infiltration of the epoxy resin takes place by capillary action. Actual experience in commercial tooling with such mats has been limited. Most promising work has been done with random fibers.

A substantial amount of work on "fiber metallurgy" has been carried out at Armour Research Foundation, and elsewhere. Portions of this work may well be applicable to plastics tooling.

Work of possible future interest centers on the production of felted metal fiber mats, densified mats, and sintered mats. According to Read,[6] "green" metal fiber felts are produced by a paper-making process. The fibers are suspended in a liquid slurry which is poured into a mold with a porous bottom. As the liquid is withdrawn by vacuum through the porous mold surface, the fibers are deposited uniformly throughout the fiber mass. If insufficient fibers are deposited at any one site, the increased permeability at that point increases the rate of flow of the slurry—and consequently, increases fiber deposition. The felts may be complex in shape, large in size, or in the form of continuous strip. Resulting porosity may be as great as 97 per cent. Densification or preforming before sintering may be obtained by normal processes such as extruding, coining or rolling.

The green felt can then be sintered in a reducing atmosphere, which produces a diffusion bond between contacting fibers, resulting in a rigid, three-dimensional fiber network of relatively high strength.

Initial data indicating properties of such metal fiber mats or structures used as reinforcement for epoxy resins are shown in Table 6.2. Note the moderately high flexural strength and impact strength, but excellent flexural modulus obtained with 75 per cent felted but unsintered aluminum fibers. Also, the exceptionally high modulus obtained with 430 stainless steel, and with unsintered long fibers of mild steel.

Strength of a "fiber metallurgy" body depends, of course, on the type of metal, degree of porosity, and whether or not the body is sintered. Also, if sintered, strength depends on the effectiveness of the diffusion bonds. Table 6.3 shows tensile strength levels obtainable at different

TABLE 6.2. METAL FIBER REINFORCEMENT OF EPOXY RESINS

Type of Metal Fiber	Volume (%)	Impact Strength (ft-lb/in. notch)	Flexure	
			Strength at Rupture (psi)	Modulus of Elasticity (10^6 psi)
None		1	8,500	0.44
Aluminum	25 [a]	3	10,000	0.7
	50 [a]	6	12,500	0.9
	75 [a]	8	17,500	2.1
430 Stainless steel	25 [a]	4	12,500	1.6
	50 [a]	6	18,000	1.8
	75 [a]	8	25,000	2.2
	83 [b]	11.5	64,300	17.0
Mild steel	50 [c]	5	59,900	16.3
Molybdenum	30 [a]	32	62,000	4.3

[a] Unbonded fibers.
[b] Bonded (sintered) fibers.
[c] Unbonded, very long fibers perpendicular to applied stress.
Source: Read.

TABLE 6.3. POROSITY AND STRENGTH OF METAL FIBER BODIES

Ultimate Tensile Strength (psi)	Porosity [a] (%)						
		430 Stainless Steel Fiber					
	Iron Fiber, P,S	Fine P,S	Fine, P,S,C,S	Fine Ann., P,S	Fine F,P,S	Medium F,P,S	Coarse F,P,S
5,000	—	55	—	—	—	—	—
7,500	50	49	—	—	—	54	—
11,000	40	39	—	34	—	40	—
15,000	30	31	—	25	38	34	36
20,000	—	20	—	16	32	28	25
25,000	—	13	25	—	27	24	16
30,000	—	—	16	—	—	21	9

[a] F = felted; P = pressed; S = sintered; C = coined.
Source: Read.[6]

porosities, and after different types of processing of iron fibers and type 430 stainless steel fibers.

HONEYCOMB STRUCTURES

Honeycomb sandwich materials have been used to only a limited extent in tooling, but the substantial benefits obtainable, both in improved tool performance and cost, would indicate a wider use for these versatile materials. The most commonly obtained benefits are probably (1) improved strength-weight characteristics, providing a stronger yet lighter tool, and (2) lower cost, since honeycomb can be used to replace a number of layers of hand-laid-up resin-impregnated cloth in a laminated tool surface.

Honeycomb sandwich materials essentially consist of two faces, with a core of honeycomb configurations in which the cells extend perpendicular to the faces. Honeycomb materials can be purchased as flat sheets consisting of core and faces for use where a flat surfaced tool is required; the approach offering the greatest diversity is to purchase the core material in the form of an expandable honeycomb. Some materials such as these, when expanded, conform to contours of relatively small radii, and when several plies of laminate are applied to each side of the core can form a honeycomb sandwich material of relatively complex configuration.

The Materials

Although a wide variety of honeycomb materials are used as structural engineering materials, honeycombs applicable for plastics tooling are usually limited to those formed from phenolic-impregnated kraft paper, aluminum foil, and glass-reinforced epoxy or polyester resin.

Paper is usually the lowest cost honeycomb core material. Paper is usually impregnated with a phenolic resin for strength and rigidity, as well as moisture resistance. Honeycombs are supplied in expanded or unexpanded form. Cell size generally ranges from ⅓ to ½ in., core thickness from ¼ to 6 inches. Density generally ranges from 1.5 to 4.0 lb/cu ft, depending on core thickness and amount of impregnated resin.

Aluminum honeycomb core materials are supplied in the expanded or unexpanded form in thicknesses of about 0.060 to 18 inches. By varying the cell size and the gage, honeycomb density can be closely controlled over a wide range. According to Stevens and Polentz,[8] aluminum core is available in cell sizes varying over a range of densities from 2 to 8 lb/cu ft and is usually supplied with perforations in the cell walls to permit gas and air flow during fabrication of the panel.

Stevens and Polentz indicate that the most common alloy used is 3003-H19, although 5052-H39 has gained wide acceptance among aircraft designers, because of its 20 per cent improvement in strength at the same density.

Glass fabric-reinforced plastics honeycomb cores are generally available in cell sizes ranging between 3/16 and ⅜ in. and in thicknesses of

0.060 to 18 inches. Such cores, of course, are supplied in the expanded form. Density for different cell sizes can be varied over a considerable range by altering fabric thickness and the amount of resin used. Densities generally range from 2.5 to 10 lb/cu ft. Some producers will precurve honeycomb cores to end-user specifications.

Designing with Honeycomb

The following brief orientation to design with honeycomb, adapted from Stevens and Polentz, provide an insight into how the materials can best be used in stressed tools.

No matter whether the core or the completed sandwich is bought, after fabrication of the tool the honeycomb area behaves as a laminated panel. The facings are the prime load-carrying members. The function of the core is to provide an essentially continuous support and stabilization for the facings, which are under tension and/or compression when the panel is loaded. At the same time the core itself must withstand shear and compressive stresses resulting from the loading.

Since honeycomb sandwich materials are almost always designed for flexural loading, the panel may be thought of as an I-beam. The panel facings represent the flanges; the core represents the web. When the panel is loaded, it undergoes the same kind of bending as the I-beam. The faces carry the tensile and compressive loads caused by bending, while the core and bonding materials prevent the facings from buckling or wrinkling under the applied load. At the same time the core and bonding layers must resist the shear loads.

Consequently, stress in the facings of a sandwich structure can be calculated by means of the basic beam formula:

$$S = Mc/I$$

where S = stress in outer fiber (psi), M = moment (in.-lb), c = distance (in.) from neutral axis to outermost fiber (½ total thickness of panel), and I = moment of inertia of section (in.^{4}).

For thin facings:

$$S = M/t_c t_f$$

where t_c = thickness of core (in.) and t_f = thickness of facings (in.). Similarly, other relationships for deflection and shear stress of simply supported beams may be applied in honeycomb design.

METAL AND CERAMIC SURFACES

The relatively poor abrasion and heat resistance, and the low thermal conductivity of plastics as compared with metals has caused a great deal of work to be directed at developing coatings for plastics molds that would improve some or all of these shortcomings. Both metallic and ceramic surface coatings have been provided. The bulk of the work is still in developmental stages. In both metal and ceramic coatings two basic approaches have been used. The first and least promising one is the application of the coating directly to the mold, the main shortcomings being that precisely consistent coating thicknesses must be obtained in order to reproduce a tool surface exactly; also, by most techniques available, adherence of the surface material to the plastic mold is relatively poor.

The second, and most promising method, is the deposition of a metallic or ceramic coating on a suitable reverse master mold, such as a plaster, and then backing the metal or ceramic surface with cast plastic. By this technique the coating surface is produced in the exact configuration of the final tool surface. Using an epoxy backing resin usually results in better plastic-to-metal or -ceramic adhesion than obtainable by depositing the metal or ceramic directly onto a cured plastic surface.

One of the important problems to remember in considering such composite tools is the differences in thermal expansion characteristics between the material used for the tool surface and the backing plastic. Usually, epoxy resins filled with metal fiber reinforcement and also metal powder can be used to bring the expansivity of the two materials closer together.

Metal Coatings

The three types of coating methods of interest for providing a metal-surfaced mold are (1) spray metallizing, (2) electroless nickel (Kanigen) plating, and (3) gas (vapor) plating. Although most work has been done with spray metallizing because of the simplicity of the process, the latter two techniques probably offer the greatest potential. They provide the best in metallurgically sound plates. Although work is now under way in developing these processes, and several successful molds (e.g., molds for plastics forming) have been made, it is fair to say that from the tooling standpoint, they are still developmental.

Spray Metallizing. In spray metallizing a wire or rod of the desired coating alloy is fed through a "gun" which melts the metal while a blast of air sprays the melted metal against the surface to be coated. Although high temperatures are used to melt the metal, the gun is held several inches from the workpiece, so that at the point of impingement of the metal particles on the mold, temperatures are quite low (so low, in fact, that a worker can hold his hand in front of the gun). However, in spraying on plaster or plastics, usually low-melting-point metals, such as aluminum, zinc, or tin, must be applied first.

The metal particles at the moment of impingement are not actually molten, but are applied with such velocity that they flatten against the surface, developing a mechanical bond. Subsequent particles develop the same type of bond with deposited particles, building up the thickness desired. Any of a variety of metals can be applied in this manner. Table 6.4 lists typical properties of several types of sprayed coatings.

TABLE 6.4. PROPERTIES OF SOME SPRAYED METAL COATINGS

	Aluminum	Brass (65:35)	Nickel	Tin	Zinc
Specific gravity	2.41	7.45	7.55	6.43	6.36
Ult. tensile strength, 1000 psi	19.5	12	17.5	—	13
Strain at ult. strength, %	0.23	0.45	0.30	—	1.43
Rockwell hardness	H72	B22	B49	—	H46
Shrinkage, in./in.	0.0068	0.009	0.008	—	0.010
Spraying speed, lb/hr	18	32	18	95	61
Spraying efficiency, % [a]	89	81	79	73	66
Major characteristics and uses [b]	Good corrosion and heat resistance	Sprays fast, good machine finish	Good corrosion resistance. Fair machine finish	Good corrosion resistance	Good all-around corrosion resistance

[a] Per cent of metal deposited.
[b] All surfaces have similar as-sprayed surfaces; surfaces differ after machining.

Major problems are difficulty in obtaining highly smooth surfaces, and lack of metallurgically consistent structure. Quality of the coating is also highly dependent on the operator's skill in controlling such factors as distance from the surface while spraying and speed of application.

Electroless Nickel (Kanigen) Process. Electroless nickel plating, originally discovered by the National Bureau of Standards and subsequently developed by the General American Transportation Co., has been widely used industrially for plating on metals. Plating on plastics and ceramics has been more limited, but it can be done. Adherence is not as good as that obtainable on metals. Probably the most successful approach is to plate a reverse plaster mold and back it with epoxy.

Essentially, the process is a method of depositing a nickel plate by reducing a nickel salt to metallic nickel, sodium hypophosphite being the usual reducing agent. The actual plate is probably a solution of nickel phosphide in nickel, usually averaging about 90 to 92 per cent nickel content; the balance is mainly phosphorus.

Theoretically, there is no limit to the thickness of coating that can be produced, thicknesses as great as 0.013 in. having been produced on a production basis. Metallurgical studies show the structure of plates to be unaffected by the nature of the substrate or thickness of plate. Growth of deposits originates from a multitude of point sources, or catalytic centers, on the surface of the base material. From these sources, coating growth proceeds at equal rates in all directions. On a properly prepared surface, the number of nuclei is so large that growth proceeds as a series of plane fronts parallel to the original surface, thereby producing a uniform thickness regardless of the contours of the part.

Compared with conventional electroplating, electroless nickel plating of nonmetallics offers 1) uniform controllable thickness, with no build-up at sharp edges and no difficulty in plating deep recesses and internal surfaces, and 2) unlimited coating thickness.

In electroless plating on plastics and ceramics, pretreatment is necessary to make the surface catalytic. Pretreatment process details are not available because a patent is being applied for. Essentially, it combines a procedure used for sensitizing surfaces for making mirrors, and a palladium dip. The object is to adsorb palladium on the surface to be plated. However, the tendency of electroless baths to decompose spontaneously when used on objects subjected to the palladium pretreatment presents problems.

In general, plates have a specific gravity of 7.9 and an as-plated hardness of Rockwell C49 (Vickers 500). When coated on metals, plates are usually heat-treated to increase hardness; e.g., treatment at 752°F for 1 hr causes a finely dispersed precipitation of nickel phosphide in the nickel coating, increasing hardness to about Rockwell C70 or 1000 Vickers. As-deposited coatings have a coefficient of thermal expansion of 7.22×10^{-6} per °F and thermal conductivity of 2.5 to 3.3 Btu/hr/sq ft/°F/ft. Coatings have limited ductility (3 to 6 per cent elongation) which can be improved by heat treatment, although treating temperatures are on the order of 1000°F.

Coatings have zero porosity in thicknesses over 0.0002 inch. Abrasion resistance is said to be excellent, as-plated wear values based on the Tabor Abrader with a C310 wheel and a 1000 g load for 5000 cycles giving an index number of 13.7, better than electrolytic nickel (14.7), but far from that of hard chromium plates (2.04).

Gas (Vapor) Plating. The term *gas plating* is synonymous with vapor plating or vapor deposition, but radically different from vacuum metallizing. Gas plating involves the chemical production of a solid or liquid coating from a gas or vapor in contact with a substrate. The reaction is generally induced by making the substrate hotter (in some cases colder) than the gas, thus disturbing the chemical equilibrium in the gas, causing a reaction that results in deposition.

Although the mechanics of the process are not new, numerous papers and articles have given engineers the impression that the process is ready for immediate, wide-scale application. Actually, with the exception of commercial chromizing and siliconizing processes, gas plating is still in the developmental stage. At present, Union Carbide Development Co., Division of Union Carbide Corp., is reported to be doing a substantial amount of evaluation work in the feasibility of the process for producing metallic surfaces on plastics tools.

Again, of the two possible approaches, i.e., plating directly on the plastic mold versus plating on a reverse plaster and backing with plastics, the latter is the most promising approach. Consequently from the tooling standpoint, the most interest lies in gas plating on plaster.

According to Powell,[5] the major benefits of the process are:

1. Any base material which is not melted or decomposed at the processing temperatures can be plated. In addition to metals, coatings have been applied to such base materials as glass, quartz, porcelain, graphite, alumina, glass fibers, silicone rubber, paper, plastics and plaster. Heat-sensitive materials such as plastics, elastomers, and paper are usually plated from easily decomposable vapors of metal carbonyls, hydrides and organometallic compounds.

2. High production rates are obtainable; in many cases, thin coatings can be applied in just a few seconds or minutes. In general, deposition rate is about 1 to 2 mils/hr.

3. Irregular surfaces can be plated. Since coatings are applied from a gaseous state they usually show less tendency than electroplates to build up on high spots or form dendrites, and less tendency than sprayed coatings to leave thinly coated edges.

4. Plates of ultra-high-purity metals and compounds, as well as alloys,

can be produced. Gas plating deposits are often purer than deposits obtainable by any other method. Also, more than one plating compound can be used in the plating atmosphere, making it possible to deposit alloys and compounds.

5. Unusual coatings that cannot be electroplated or applied in a nonporous condition by other methods can be deposited. For example, the method can be used to plate refractory compounds such as the transition metal carbides, nitrides, borides and silicides, in addition to titanium, zirconium, columbium, tantalum, molybdenum and tungsten.

Of the three methods of applying plates by gas methods (i.e., hydrogen reduction, thermal decomposition, and displacement plating), thermal decomposition is the one receiving the most attention for tooling applications. The operating temperature required in thermal decomposition plating varies widely depending on the plating material. Hydrides, carbonyls and organometallic compounds are decomposed at temperatures ranging from a low of 300°F to a high of 1150°F; metal iodides at 1650 to 2550°F; and metal bromides and chlorides at temperatures ranging from 2200 to 3650°F.

Probably the bulk of commercial interest has centered around nickel. Nickel is readily deposited in an adherent, ductile form by the thermal decomposition of nickel tetracarbonyl at temperatures of only 350 to 390°F. The coating atmosphere can consist of pure nickel carbonyl vapor, or of a nonoxidizing carrier gas containing at least 4 per cent nickel carbonyl. Large objects are best coated by blowing the coating atmosphere against the specimen through water-cooled nozzles. The low decomposition temperatures permit rapid efficient heating of the base material with infrared lamps.

According to Powell,[5] coatings deposited by gas plating are more or less crystalline. Crystallites deposited at low temperatures are so small that the plate is virtually amorphous. In contrast, crystals deposited at high temperatures can range up to ¼ in. or more in diameter, depending on coating thickness. In general, size of crystals tends to increase with plate thickness.

Thickness of plates can range from a few millionths of an inch to ¼ in. or more. Coatings intended to provide hardness and resistance to scoring and abrasion are usually not made over 1 mil thick so that they retain some flexibility.

Some of the more important problems and limitations of the process include: (1) plating compounds tend to be unstable, and some are highly toxic and volatile, (2) plates may be nonuniform, thickness variations of 10 to 25 per cent being common, and (3) undesirable side reactions are possible.

Ceramic Coatings

J. Mele of Grumman recently reported on successful work in using ceramic surfaces for plastics tools. Coatings are primarily used to provide high-temperature resistance in specific areas of such tools as welding jigs and fixtures. Aluminum oxide and zirconium oxide are the two ceramics which have been used most commonly. Alumina is the less expensive coating; zirconia the more heat resistant.

The coatings are applied by flame spraying techniques similar to those used in metal spraying. Two similar ceramic flame spraying techniques were developed several years ago by the Norton Co. ("Rokide" coatings), and Armour Research Foundation, working independently. The ceramic material either in the form of rod or powder is fed to the flame spray gun where it is melted and sprayed onto the surface. Again, the temperature of the surface against which the ceramic particles impinge is substantially lower than the melting point of the ceramic. For example, Mele points out that with the proper application technique, the surface of the plastic or plaster can be maintained at 400°F. Of course, this involves intermittent spraying, and techniques are not completely developed. Problems still exist in obtaining a coating of maximum adherence to the plastic without charring or distorting the plastic base.

Mele indicates that two techniques can be used: the first involves development of the reverse plaster mold, spraying the ceramic on the plaster in the areas desired, then building up the plastic around the ceramic areas. With such a technique, the ceramic portion of the tool is produced with the final desired dimensions and surface. The second technique of spraying directly on the plastic is useful for tools where dimensional and surface accuracy of the ceramic portions are not critical.

Properties of Coatings. Table 6.5 lists properties of alumina and zirconia flame-sprayed coatings. Alumina coatings provide, in addition to excellent heat resistance, good thermal insulation, and high resistance to wear and abrasion. They are applied at lower temperatures than zirconia. Alumina coatings have a high macrohardness, which is equivalent to Rockwell C45. Despite the fact that the coatings adhere to substrates by only mechanical means, adhesion and impact strength are reported to be quite good, e.g., a 1/16-in. sheet metal with an 0.010 in. coating can be bent 45 degrees with no evidence of failure.

Thickness of alumina coatings usually ranges from 0.001 to 0.050 in.,

TABLE 6.5. FLAME-SPRAYED CERAMIC COATINGS

	Aluminum Oxide	Zirconium Oxide
Application Properties		
Deposition rate, sq ft/hr/10 mils	15-16	4-10
Thickness range, mils	5-50 [a]	5-50 [b]
Finish after polishing, μin.rms	2-50 [c]	15-50 [c]
Thermal Properties		
Melting point, °F	3600-3700	4500-4600
Coefficient of thermal expansion, 10^{-6}/°F	4.0-4.3 [c]	
Thermal conductivity, Btu/hr/sq ft/°F/in.	19-20	7-8
Shock resistance	Good	Very good
Other Properties		
Dielectric strength, v/mil	200	100 [d]
Vickers hardness (DPH, 25-g load)	1400	400
Porosity, %	8-12	8-12
Density, lb/cu in.	0.12	0.19

[a] Thicknesses up to 0.125 in. can be produced for special applications.
[b] Thicknesses over 0.10 in. can be produced for special applications.
[c] Varies with method of application.
[d] Nonconductive at room temperature; conductivity increases rapidly above 2190°F.
Source: Materials Selector Issue, 1959-60, *Materials in Design Engineering.*

though thicker coatings can be applied. Where the coating is applied directly to the plastic and forms the finished surface on a tool area, as-sprayed surface finish obtainable is generally upward of 125 microinch rms. Finishes of 1 to 2 microinch rms are obtainable by diamond lapping.

Zirconia coatings withstand higher temperatures than alumina, but are not as hard nor as abrasion-resistant. Combined with the higher heat resistance is a lower thermal conductivity than that of alumina, providing improved thermal insulation. But zirconia also has higher thermal expansion than alumina. Thicknesses generally range from 0.005 to 0.050 in., but thicknesses of 0.010 in. are frequently used to increase resistance to impact.

REFERENCES

1. Chinn, J. L., "Electroless Nickel Plating," *Materials in Design Engineering,* p. 104 (May 1955).
2. Fabian, R. J., "Porcelain Enamels and Ceramic Coatings," *Materials in Design Engineering,* p. 103 (July 1958).
3. Gutzeit, G., "Kanigen Nickel Plating," *Metal Progress,* p. 113 (July 1954).
4. Powell, C. F., Campbell, I. E., Gonser, B. W., "Vapor-Plating," New York, John Wiley & Sons, Inc., 1955.

5. Powell, C. F., "Gas Plating," *Materials in Design Engineering,* p. 98 (Jan. 1960).
6. Read, R. H., "Fiber Metallurgy, A Progress Report," *Materials in Design Engineering,* p. 104 (Dec. 1959).
7. Riley, M. W., "Engineer's Guide to Industrial Textiles," *Materials in Design Engineering,* p. 115 (July 1959).
8. Stevens, P. J. B., and Polentz, L. M., "Honeycomb, How to Design, What Materials to Use, Part 1," *Materials in Design Engineering* (Mar. 1960).
9. *Symposium on Electroless Nickel Plating, ASTM Special Technical Publication No. 265,* American Society for Testing Materials, Philadelphia, 1959.
10. Mazzucchelli, A. P., "New Fiber-Reinforced Epoxy Compositions," paper presented before the Society of The Plastics Industry, Inc., Reinforced Plastics Div., 13th Annual Conference, Feb. 1958.

7. *General Fabricating Techniques*

The most common forms of tooling plastics are (1) gravity, vacuum or pressure castings, which may be unfilled, filled, or reinforced with short random fibers, and (2) reinforced plastics, which may consist of cloth or mat reinforcement, or sprayed chopped glass or metal fibers.

A variety of techniques is used to produce these forms. The methods discussed here are the most commonly used. Specific modifications of fabricating techniques to meet specialized tooling requirements are discussed in subsequent chapters on the various types of tools.

Pattern or Mold Fabrication

Since one of the most important attributes of plastics for tools is their ability exactly to reproduce a surface simply and in detail at room temperature, the original surface to be reproduced (or the pattern) is critical. A tool can only be as accurate as its pattern. A variety of pattern materials can be used; conventional plaster or wood is probably the most common. Metal or plastic prototype parts, or plaster or plastic patterns splined by the loft template method can be used.

Wooden patterns or models can be used either directly as the mold for plastics tools, or as a pattern from which to obtain a plastic or plaster mold used to produce a duplicate of the original wooden pattern. Conventional wooden pattern-making techniques are used. But when wood is used directly for forming the plastics, it must be thoroughly dried and sealed to prevent gassing and adhesion of the plastics material.

Plastics molds for plastics tools are becoming quite widely used. The benefits of plastics over plaster molds for producing a plastics tool is that they are lighter, stronger and can be reused a number of times, although they are generally more expensive. Economic considerations of each specific job will dictate the selection of plastics or plaster.

Plaster Mold or Pattern Fabrication. Because of the importance of the original surface, the general plaster fabricating techniques are briefly described here. The discussion is concerned primarily with hard gypsum cements rather than soft plasters, such as plaster of Paris.

The variables that must be controlled to obtain best performance in plaster patterns are (1) consistency, or water-to-plaster ratio, (2) mixing time and technique, and (3) shop housekeeping, including such factors as cleanliness of water, mixing containers, and storage areas.

Normal consistency of any plaster is expressed by the amount of water required to mix 100 parts of the plaster by weight to a standard fluidity. By changes in normal consistency alone, compressive strengths can vary from 1000 to 15,000 psi. Compressive strength is critical as it correlates closely with abrasion resistance and resulting length of useful life.

Theoretically, according to Young,[5] only 18.6 lb of water will convert 100 lb of plaster to 118.6 lb of cured gypsum. Actually more water is always necessary to produce a usable slurry. Consequently excess water is always present in any freshly set mass of gypsum. The more water used in mixing, the weaker the set mass. For example, if 80 lb of water are mixed with 100 lb of plaster, dry compressive strength is about 1500 psi; if 30 lb of water are used the compressive strength is about 11,000 psi.

For best results, water and plaster should be weighed carefully to provide proper consistency in production quantities. Plaster should always be added to the water; under no condition should water be added to the plaster. After adding the plaster, it should be allowed to set undisturbed for 2 to 5 min. The mix should then be stirred thoroughly so that all the plaster particles are wet, removing the film of entrapped air that inevitably surrounds each grain of powder. Quantities of 5 to 15 lb are usually mixed by hand; larger mixing operations can be carried out with a direct-drive, 1760 rpm propeller mixer. A ⅓-hp motor driving a 3-in., 3-blade, 25-degree pitch propeller is satisfactory for batches up to 50 lb; for batches of 50 to 100 lb, slurry rotation should be such that the propeller will force the mix downward and the propeller should clear the bottom of the bucket by 1 to 2 inches.

Mixing should be carried out until the plaster has creamed or thickened slightly. This normally requires from 2 to 5 min. Setting time for the cast plaster is affected by the consistency. Normally the cast gypsum plaster can be removed from the pattern within 25 to 30 min. after pouring. Setting time can be shortened by using warm water (160 to 180°F), or by longer mixing. Colder water (50 to 60°F) will extend the period of fluidity or set of the cements without affecting final properties.

Plasters expand, rather than shrink, on setting. Expansion characteristics vary widely depending on the type of plaster used. Plasters are available with expansion characteristics ranging from a low of 0.002

in./ft to a high of about 1/4 in./ft, providing materials to suit a variety of specific tooling needs.

There are three basic methods of fabricating plaster models, the loft template, splash cast, and solid cast. They are briefly outlined below.

Loft template method. The loft template tooling method is often used for constructing original master models, prototype patterns and die patterns. It is particularly adapted to production of nonsymmetrical shapes. More recently, plastics have been used also for splining.

Standard dimension contour or template lines are photographed or drawn on rigid 1/16- to 1/4-in. steel or aluminum sheets. Templates are then cut to dimensions on a metal cutting band saw and then hand- or machine-filed to a smooth contour. The working edge of the template must be free of file marks, scratches, center punch marks or other flaws that would reproduce on the model surface. Lightening or ventilation holes should be cut in the templates before they are erected. These holes are important in providing proper ventilation for full setting of the plaster. If the model is to be a permanent reference tool, the steel or aluminum templates should be coated to prevent corrosion at points where the plaster contacts the metal.

Templates should be mounted on a rigid, dimensionally stable, moisture-resistant base, e.g., reinforced plaster, steel, or aluminum. Plywood, mahogany or hard wood should not be used as the moisture from the cement is likely to warp the base.

Templates should be bolted together to prevent movement, then tied to the base with ties of fiber impregnated with plaster. Reinforcement most commonly used is uncarded, long-fiber hemp. The hemp is matted in baling, so it must be picked apart to loosen the individual strengths. A handful of strands is dipped into the gypsum cement mix and formed into a rope to tie the templates to the base. Expanded metal is then used to span the openings between templates and act as a support for the plaster. Strands of hemp are made into flat batts and dipped into the plaster mix to thoroughly saturate them. They are then laid over the expanded metal. After the batt is applied, another mix of plaster is screeded in with a saw tooth scraper to build up a uniform striated surface. The rough surface produces a good mechanical bond, as well as an integral crystalline bond with the final plaster mix.

The final mix is applied and wiped or screeded in, using the contours of the templates to form a smooth accurately contoured finished surface. Necessary reference and trim lines are scribed before the model is given two coats of clear lacquer.

The loft template method of producing patterns or molds can also be used by spining with plastics as shown in the composite sketch in Figure 7.1. The basic technique is the same as that used with plaster, except that a thixotropic epoxy resin is used instead of plaster. The templates are erected in the same manner, and usually tied in or braced with reinforced plastics tubing.

The screening material used to span the areas between templates may be hardware cloth, expanded metal, or glass fabric. The thixotropic resin is then applied and screeded in a manner similar to that used for plaster. The major problem is to get the resin system to the proper consistency

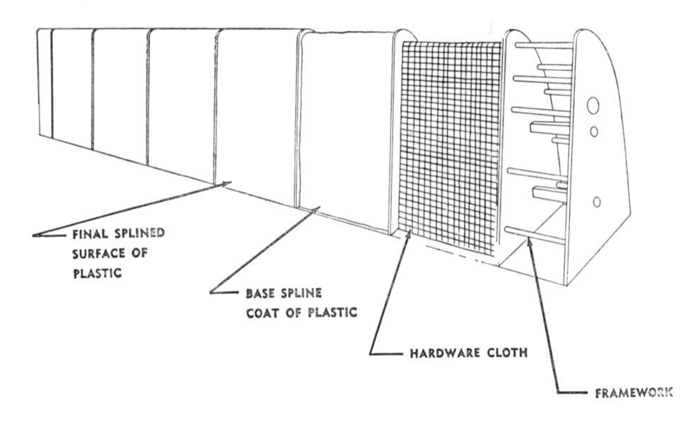

Figure 7.1. Composite sketch shows steps in loft template pattern making with plastics. Section at right shows erected templates and framework, with (from right to left) applied hardware cloth, base spline coat, and final spline coat. (*Rezolin, Inc.*)

to minimize run-off yet get maximum workability. Some workers report difficulty in obtaining this compromise. However, a variety of formulators have prepackaged systems suitable for such work.

In considering plastics *vs.* plaster for the loft template pattern or mold, it should be kept in mind that although plastics may be higher in cost than plaster, plastics provide lighter weight, higher strength and durability, and longer life. The benefits of each should be evaluated in the light of the specific tool.

Splash Cast Method. A suitable parting compound is applied to the original model or pattern. Heavy cardboard or plywood strips are cut and assembled around the model surface to provide a box in which to make the splash cast. Since the plaster splash section should be 1 to 2 in., the box should extend 1½ to 2 in. above the surface to be reproduced.

A mix of the proper plaster is poured slowly over the entire surface of the model to form a ¼- to ½-in. layer. During pouring, the model should be joggled or vibrated to eliminate flow marks and entrapped air.

After this mix has progressed from the free-flowing to the plastic stage, a second mix should be prepared. Fiber batts approximately ½ in. thick are dipped into the mix and then placed over the entire pattern surface. Average size patterns will require 5 to 10 batts to provide proper reinforcement; larger patterns will require more.

A wooden or metal frame is then constructed to serve as structural reinforcement for the pattern. This frame is mounted on height gage blocks and is fastened to the pattern with fiber ties, which are dipped in a third mix of plaster. If a large number of ties or "legs" are required to fasten the frame to the pattern, a fourth final plaster mix may be necessary to properly coat the ties and fasten them securely to the pattern.

After the final mix has set thoroughly, removal of the pattern can be aided by wedging evenly around the surface or by gently blowing apart with compressed air.

Solid Cast Method. Small plaster patterns 2 to 3 in. thick are usually cast solid. A wooden frame is constructed around the model and the plaster is poured slowly into one of the four corners so that it will flow across the model. Pouring this way eliminates entrapment of air and prevents small voids or holes in the pattern surface. Never pour directly on the model as the turbulence is apt to create streaks or flow marks. Joggling or vibrating the model while pouring is recommended.

When the mix has set, the wooden frame is removed, the cast turned over and the model removed.

Where time is critical, plaster molds can be used as-cast. However, drying molds prior to use is highly recommended to obtain optimum strength and surface hardness. Drying time varies with the type of plaster and thickness of mold. Hard gypsum cement molds should be dried at about 110 to 120°F (do not exceed 125°F) for 20 to 30 hr for thicknesses of 1 to 1½ in., 30 to 48 hr for thicknesses of 1½ to 2½ in., and 48 to 72 hr for 2½ to 4 in. thicknesses.

Other Techniques. Tooling with plaster is a profession in itself. This summary is only intended to outline briefly some of the most important techniques. Auxiliary techniques, such as the use of sheet wax to build up metal thickness, are well understood by competent plaster model and pattern makers, and will not be discussed here.

Mold Preparation

Proper preparation of the surface of the mold or pattern is essential to producing a plastic tool with a high quality working surface. (Materials suppliers will be glad to recommend and/or supply proper surface-preparation materials and parting compounds.)

In general, for plastic, wooden or plaster molds, surfaces should be lightly sanded, brushed and wiped, then washed with a toluene-soaked rag, then allowed to dry. Where extremely smooth and glossy surfaces are required, all defects and pinholes should be repaired with modeling clay or hard wax. For wooden and plaster molds a proper sealant should then be applied and allowed to dry.

The proper type of parting compound to be used depends on the type of mold material, the type of resin system used for the tool, temperatures and pressures to be used (if any) during molding of tool, and the type of application method most economical for the particular shop.

On porous molds, such as plaster and wood, film or film-forming parting agents should be used. (Note: on green or undried plaster molds, polyvinyl alcohol cannot be used.) On nonporous molds, such as metal, the parting agent may be a lubricant type. The type of resin used in the tool also affects the type of parting compound used. For example, a styrene-containing polyester resin would attack any parting compound soluble in styrene.

Some typical parting agents, as given in the "SPI Plastics Engineering Handbook" are: (1) films, such as polyvinyl alcohol, cellulose, glassine paper, and water-soluble modified styrene; (2) film-forming materials, such as agar-agar, cellulose acetate, polyvinyl alcohol, waxes, methyl cellulose and carboxymethyl cellulose; (3) lubricants, such as silicones, sulfate esters, graphites, monoalkyl and dialkyl phosphate, stearic acid, and petroleum jelly.

Some of the most commonly used successful parting compounds for epoxy resins are the polyvinyl alcohol films and the silicone lubricants. Plastics formulators have been quite active in developing different types of proprietary parting compounds. For example, one formulator reports development of an all-purpose paste-type parting compound which is merely rubbed on the mold and wiped down prior to casting or laminating the plastics tool. Formulators should be consulted for details.

Reinforced Plastics Fabrication Techniques

Reinforced plastics are used where a tool requires maximum strength and dimensional stability. The technology of reinforced plastics is large and complex. For the types of structures required in tooling, only certain materials and techniques are commonly used, reducing somewhat the number of variables that must be considered. But still, the production of quality reinforced plastics for tool surfaces is dependent on careful workmanship and proper control of the many variables affecting the finished part. These variables include type of resin system, type and form of reinforcement, type of forming method and curing conditions.

This section refers to reinforced plastics used primarily for tool surfaces. It includes fabricating techniques for producing both (1) cloth or mat-reinforced laminates and (2) spray-molded surfaces, which include chopped glass or metal strand reinforcement. Such materials as mass cast chopped fiber filled plastics are actually "reinforced plastics," but, because of the methods used in their fabrication, are discussed under the section on casting plastics.

Laminating. In the reinforced plastics industry, laminating is accomplished by either the "dry lay-up" or "wet lay-up" technique. Dry lay-up, not used at present for tooling, makes use of plies of reinforcing cloth or mat which have been preimpregnated or saturated with resins which have been B-staged (i.e., partially cured) to form a relatively dry sheet of reinforced material. Layers of this so-called "prepreg" material are laid up to the desired thickness, and molded under heat and pressure. The heat initially softens the B-staged resin, permitting it to fuse to other layers, and finally finish-cures the resin to the final state.

Because of such factors as higher materials costs and the higher pressures required to mold prepreg, the dry lay-up techniques are as a rule not used for tooling laminates.

Wet lay-up involves the saturation or impregnation of the glass cloth or mat at the time of, or immediately prior to, lay-up in the mold. After building up the desired laminate thickness, cure of the resin is carried out either with no additional pressure (contact molding), or at the low 10 to 14-psi pressures obtained by vacuum bag molding.

Contact molding is more commonly used in producing tooling laminates. Bag molding requires a polyvinyl alcohol "bag" or film which is placed over the completed laminate. A vacuum is then drawn within the bag during cure. One disadvantage of the vacuum bag technique is that the laminate must be cured before any supporting structure is attached. In many tool fabrications, such supporting structures are tied into the back of the laminate prior to its cure. However, the additional pressures obtained by vacuum bagging do permit a higher glass content in the laminate improving physical properties. Maximum glass content for contact molding is about 30 per cent for mat, 50 per cent for cloth; maximum glass content for vacuum bag moldings is about 35 per cent for mat and 55 per cent for cloth.

Whether the laminate is to be cured by contact or vacuum pressures, hand lay up procedures are the same. These are shown in flow chart form in Figure 7.2.

The first step is the preparation of the mold. If the pattern or mold is convex, a dam made of wood, cardboard or reinforced plastics is

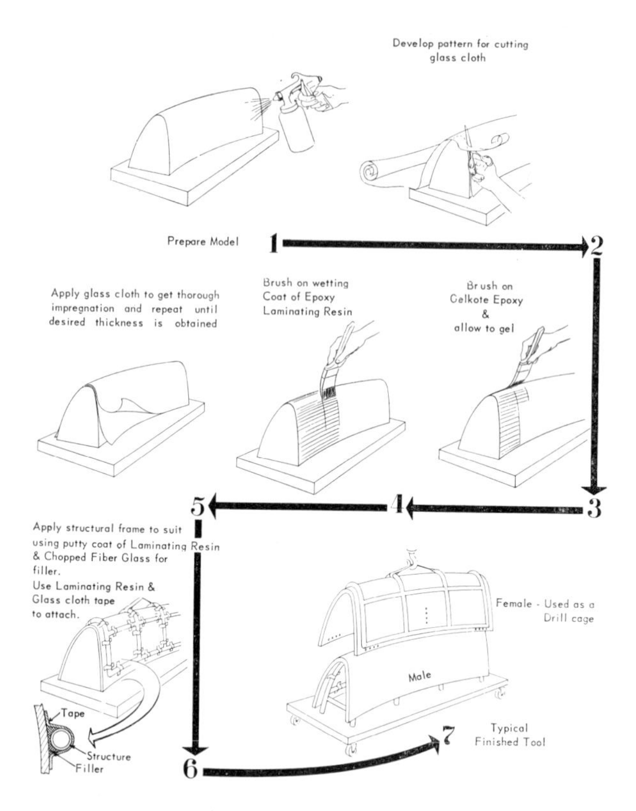

Figure 7.2. Typical steps in fabricating a laminated tool, in this case a drill cage. First step shows treatment of mold with sealer, parting agent and release wax. (*Rezolin, Inc.*)

usually built up around the pattern. Or, use of a highly thixotropic surface gel coat may in some cases preclude this step. The entire mold is then prepared with the proper parting agent system, as described earlier.

Before mixing the resin, the glass cloth or mat must be carefully tailored to the contour of the pattern or mold. In using cloth, the weave of the fabric must be considered and the cloth tailored so that the direction of the stronger yarns in the fabric is parallel to the primary load-bearing direction in the final tool. Where essentially isotropic high strengths are desired, the cloth should be arranged so that the warp direction in each ply is either at 90 degrees to the warp direction in the preceding ply, or for maximum isotropic characteristics, 45 degrees. Where only low strengths are required, mat reinforcements provide the maximum in isotropic characteristics.

In pretailoring the fabric, each piece is cut to cover the maximum surface area without wrinkling. A generous overlap of cloth must be allowed where one piece of cloth meets another. In succeeding plies, the points of overlap, or joints, should be staggered so that laps are not in the same location from layer to layer. All the cloth to be used in the laminate should be tailored in this way prior to mixing the resin. Laminate thickness usually ranges from $\frac{3}{16}$ to $\frac{1}{4}$ inch.

After tailoring the glass, a gel coat is usually used as the surface coat on the mold. This is usually a thixotropic formulation of the laminating resin. Such a surface coat eliminates "show-through" of the reinforcement, and can be used to provide specific surface characteristics. Gel coats can be formulated by filling and/or chemical modification to provide such characteristics as improved abrasion resistance, hardness or resilience, or color.

The gel coat resin should be mixed slowly to prevent formation of air bubbles. One pint of surface or gel-coat resin will cover approximately 144 sq in. to a thickness of $\frac{1}{8}$ inch. Depending on the pot life of the system, the mixture can be allowed to stand for a short period of time, or used immediately. The longer the time elapsing between mixing and applying, the shorter is the curing time on the model.

The gel coat should be applied by brushing or spraying in a thin, smooth coat, covering the entire surface of the mold. While waiting for the gel coat to become tacky, low spots should be checked periodically for resin build-up; such areas are to be smoothed out when this occurs. Areas of resin concentration will not be reinforced by fibers, and may result in chipping of the tool face in service. In sharp corners, a chopped or milled glass fiber-resin putty may be used to build up a smooth fillet. This will simplify draping the cloth in the mold. When the gel coat has cured sufficiently to dent but will not stick to the fingers, it is ready for the first layer of glass cloth or mat.

Laminating resin and hardener are then mixed and applied immediately to the gel coat. The glass cloth or mat is fitted over the layer of resin, and another layer of resin applied to the back of the reinforcement. The reinforcement should be smoothed and pressed by hand, spatula, or brush until all trapped air is worked out, and the cloth or mat has been completely saturated with the resin. The reinforcement must be worked well down into corners and valleys.

When one layer is thoroughly saturated and smoothed down, subsequent layers of cloth or mat are applied in the same manner, a coat of resin and a layer of reinforcement, until the desired thickness is attained. The final coat of resin should be heavy enough to provide a smooth, continuous inner resin surface, and also to assist in bonding any backing or supporting structure. Although thickness of tooling laminates is commonly about $\frac{3}{16}$ to $\frac{1}{4}$ in., thickness may be increased up to about $\frac{1}{2}$ in. or more if required. When using epoxies, care must be taken that thickness is not such to cause excessive exotherm.

When the resin starts to gel in the pot during the lay-up process, it should be discarded and a new batch prepared. Partially gelled resin will not saturate the reinforcement completely, resulting in voids; also, previously applied resin will be picked up by the brush.

Metallic and nonmetallic inserts can be molded in place during lay-up, or potted in place in a cured laminate. A common procedure for molding bushings in place is by using locating pins. Before applying the gel coat to the mold, $\frac{1}{16}$-in. pilot holes are drilled in the model at each point where a bushing is required. Wax-coated locating pins are inserted into each hole. After the resin surface coat has been applied, knurled bushings are slid over each pin. The desired number of glass cloth layers are laminated, cutting around the bushings and packing glass roving and resin in areas where the glass cloth cannot reach, e.g., between bushings set close together. The completed laminate is allowed to cure overnight before removing locating pins.

When inserting a bushing in a finished laminate, an oversized hole is drilled out at the point where the bushing is to be located; the bushing is inserted and potted in place with resin putty or paste.

All bushings or other inserts should be cleaned thoroughly prior to use. Knurling or other means of mechanically keying the bushing to the plastic will improve bonds. All bushing manufacturers produce special bushings for use with reinforced plastics; many specialty bushings are also supplied by resin formulators. For example, a patented specialty bushing for drill jigs changes color on excessive heating, providing a warning that the bushing is overheated.

Once the hand lay-up has been completed, any of a number of procedures can be followed, depending on the type of tool construction: (1) the laminate can be cured either at room temperature or with heat, or a vacuum bag can be applied and the laminate bag molded, or (2) core or backing structures can be applied to the back of the laminate before the final resin surface has cured. Selection and fabrication of such cores and backings is discussed in a subsequent section of this chapter.

Spray Molding. A relatively recent technique is the method of spraying resin and chopped strand reinforcement against a mold to build up a reinforced plastic surface. It is a lower-cost, more rapid technique than hand lay-up, but strengths of parts are more similar to those of mat-reinforced laminates (when properly fabricated) than to cloth. Typical properties of polyester and epoxy spray-up laminates are shown in Table 7.1.

TABLE 7.1. TYPICAL PROPERTIES OF SPRAY-MOLDED LAMINATES

	Polyester [a]	Epoxy [b]
Flexural strength, 1000 psi	11.7-18.8	26.7
Flexural modulus of elasticity, 10^5 psi	6.7-7.0	9.6
After 2 hr in boiling water:		
Flexural strength, 1000 psi	10.3-11.9	21.5
Flexural modulus of elasticity, 10^5 psi	4.1-3.3	7.7
Izod impact strength, ft-lb/in. notch	4-6	6.7
Water absorption (24 hr), %	0.7-1.5	0.33

[a] Resin content ranges from 58.3 to 78.7 per cent; specimens postcured 2 hr at 250°F.
[b] Resin content is 78.4 per cent; specimens postcured 2 hr at 300°F.
Source: Union Carbide Plastics Co., Div. of Union Carbide Corp.

Most widely used with glass, the technique essentially is as follows. Roving is drawn from a creel, fed through a hand chopper gun and blown at the mold. Resin system ingredients are injected into the glass stream by either of two basic types of spray guns; the first, developed for polyester resins, employs two metering nozzles—one carrying resin premixed with catalyst, the other carrying resin premixed with accelerator. In the second gun, designed for epoxies, ingredients are fed separately into a mixing chamber just ahead of the single spray nozzle. By either method the resin mix coats the glass strands, and the merged spray is directed evenly into the mold by the operator. The glass-resin mass thus applied is then rolled, but by hand, to remove air and pack the mix to uniform thickness.

Although glass content as high as 50 to 55 per cent has been achieved in certain applications, the more common maximum glass content is about 35 per cent; most production molders prefer about 29 per cent glass. The lower glass content, though providing lower strengths, permits ample resin for thoroughly wetting the reinforcement, giving good bonds in all sections of the part.

A newer approach to spray molding, but one that appears highly promising, is the use of spray guns to spray metal fibers. As of late 1960, there are two approaches. The first is flocking of metal fibers over the entire back of a surface gel coat which has just been applied to the mold. Metal- or glass fiber-filled epoxy resin is then pressure-cast against the back of the gel coat to produce the finished tool. Properties of tools produced in this manner are discussed in the section on pressure casting in Chapter 4.

The second approach is the use of metal fibers in fabricating plastics-faced plaster models, patterns and molds. The master pattern or mold is first prepared in the conventional manner. A face or gel coat is brushed on, but before it sets metal fibers are sprayed or flocked onto the back of the gel coat. After the gel coat has hardened, a brush coat of plaster is applied, and while still wet, plaster is cast against it. The technique combines the economies of plaster with a hard, impact-resistant surface of fiber-reinforced resin. The metal fibers also provide an interlocking bond between plastic and plaster. Such a tool is low in cost, but heavier and not as durable as the all-plastic type.

Casting Tools

A fundamental understanding of good foundry practice is helpful in casting plastics. Although plastics are mixed and cast at room temperature, many problems such as flow of material, exclusion of bubbles and voids, and complete mold filling are similar to those encountered by the foundryman.

The most widely used type of casting for plastics tooling is gravity casting of either tool surfaces or masses. Newer techniques involving either pressure or vacuum are promising.

Surface Casting. Essentially, surface casting is a technique of casting liquid resin between the master pattern or mold and a suitable core material. The result is a tool with an unreinforced plastic surface. The core may be iron, steel or fabricated boiler plate, aggregate, or cast resin. Where weight is important, the core may be of plastic foam.

Both epoxy and phenolic casting resins are used. Epoxies offer the benefit of versatility in that they can be formulated to provide either a hard, rigid surface or a surface with a high degree of resilience. A metal core offers distinct benefits in surface casting epoxies in that its thermal conductivity helps dissipate exotherm during cure of the epoxy. Surface cast epoxies are generally applied in thicknesses of $\frac{1}{16}$ to $\frac{3}{4}$ inch.

Cast phenolic surfaces may be used where relatively thick cast faces are required with a high degree of rigidity and hardness. Often where a lightweight foam core is required the tool surface must be harder and more rigid to bear the loads. A 2 to 4- in. thick cast phenolic surface may be a highly economical answer. The flow chart in Figure 7.3 shows the typical technique for surface-casting phenolic on a foam core.

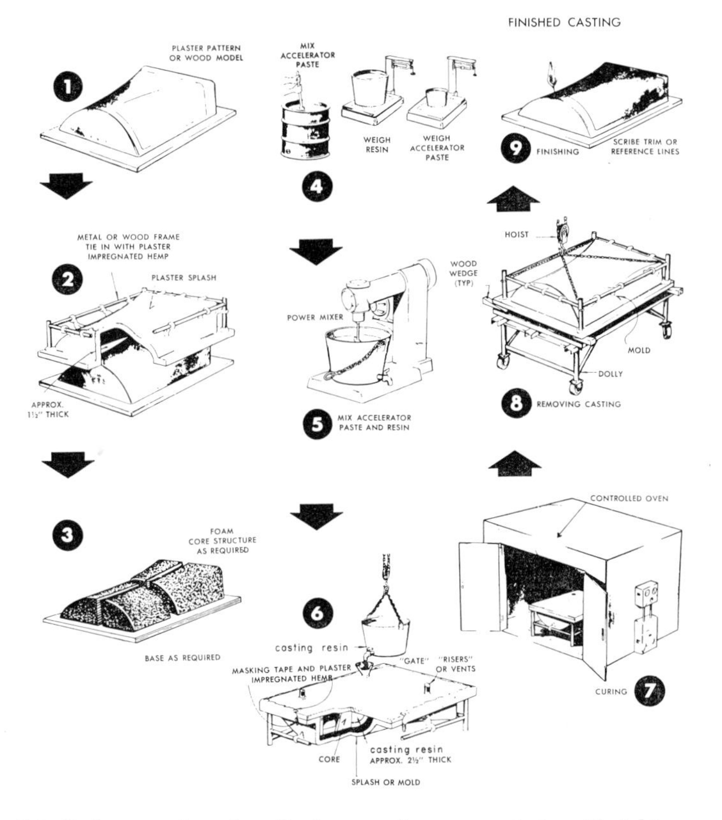

Figure 7.3. Surface casting phenolic face on foam core starts with taking a plaster splash from pattern or model, preforming a proper phenolic core undersized, attaching core to base, and suspending it in plaster splash. Casting resin is mixed and cast between core and mold surface, and oven cured. (*Rezolin, Inc.*)

Figure 7.4 shows a typical setup and procedure for casting an epoxy surface on a metal core. Figure 7.5 shows a finished drop hammer punch and die, produced by this technique. (Note in Figure 7.5 the common method of using a flexible epoxy face on the punch and a rigid face on the die.)

Molds for surface castings are prepared in the same way as molds for laminating; again, the degree of finishing required of the mold surface is dependent on the finish required on the tool, as determined by that required on the production part.

When using a metal core, preparation of the metal surface prior to casting is critical in obtaining a sound bond between metal and plastics, and consequently obtaining a sound tool. Surfaces should be sandblasted or otherwise roughsanded both to remove scale, oil, wax and other contaminants, and to rough the surface to improve the metal-resin bond. After

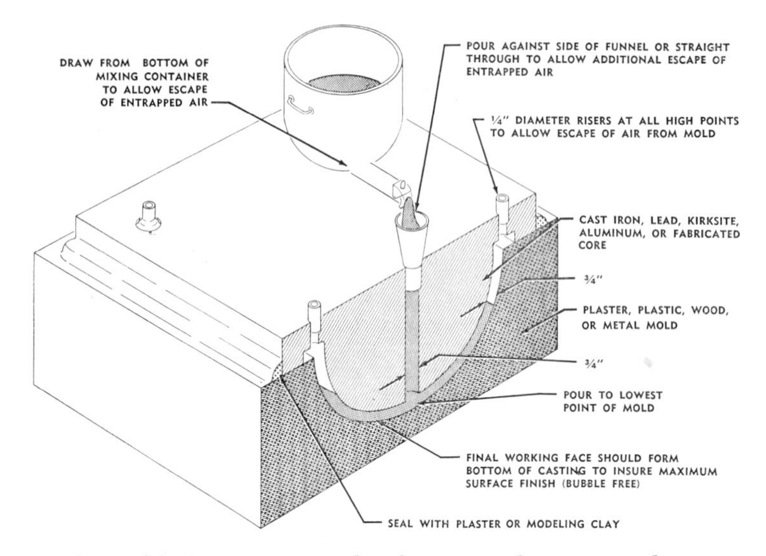

Figure 7.4. For cast epoxy tool surface on metal core, suspend core in mold and pour as shown. (*Rezolin, Inc.*)

such cleaning, care should be taken to avoid recontamination; e.g., even fingerprints will prevent optimum bonding. If the surface is not to be cast immediately after the core is prepared, the metal surface should be coated with an epoxy paint to prevent recontamination. When surface-casting phenolics, a coating (e.g., epoxy) should be applied to the metal to protect it from the acidic catalysts used with phenolics.

In setting up the mold for a surface pour, the important principle to keep in mind is that the casting resin must enter at the lowest point of the mold, and provisions must be made for the escape of all the air in the mold. First the core should be suspended within the female mold with clearance between mold and core sufficient for the desired thickness of the cast face. The mold should be so located that the final working face of the tool is formed by the bottom of the casting. In this way possibility of surface voids or bubbles is minimized.

Ample gates and risers must be provided in the proper locations. For example, as shown in Figure 7.3, for a 2¾-in. cast face, gates should be about ¾ in. in diameter, feeding to the lowest point in the mold. Risers should be about ¼ in. in diameter, located at all high points of the mold. After mixing the casting resin and hardeners or catalysts, provisions should be made to draw the mix from the bottom of the mixing container to allow escape of air entrapped during mixing. Pouring should be against

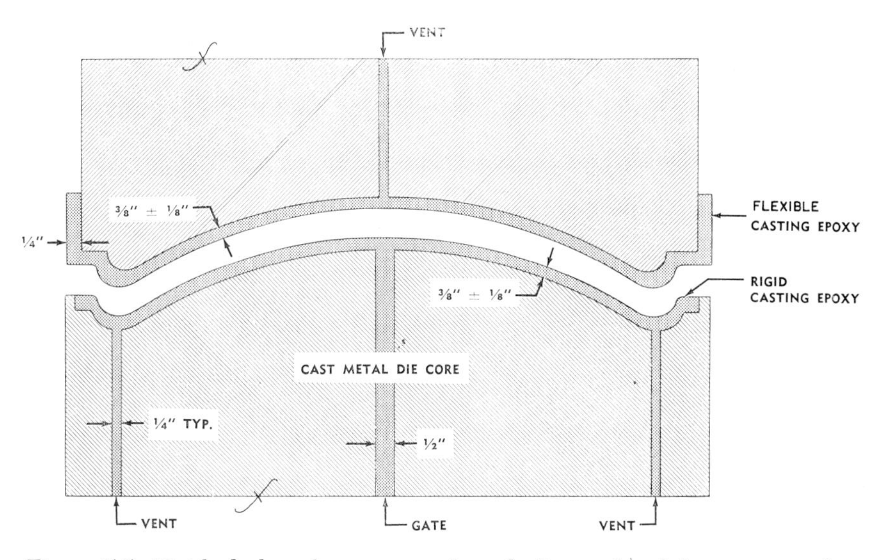

Figure 7.5. Finished drop hammer punch and die produced by epoxy surface casting technique. Use of flexible epoxy face on punch precludes allowance for metal thickness in casting punch face against die. (*Rezolin, Inc.*)

the side of the gate funnel or straight through the sprue to allow the most air to escape from the mold.

Metal or laminated plastics inserts can be incorporated in the cast surface either by attaching the insert to the mold in the proper position and casting around it, or potting in place in the finished casting, using the same casting material. Metal inserts should receive the same careful preparation as cores, i.e., both cleaning and roughing, and coating for protection when using phenolic casting resins.

Mass Casting. Phenolics are most commonly used for those tools requiring massive solid castings. Epoxies can be properly formulated so that exotherm is tolerable, but the materials cost becomes quite high unless the resins are highly filled. Phenolics are substantially lower in cost, though they usually require an oven cure and are quite brittle.

Mass casting techniques are similar to those employed in surface casting, except that no core is used. The primary precaution is to exclude all air from the casting. Mixing of ingredients should be slow; the mold should be filled from the lowest point; splashing and turbulence should be meticulously avoided during pouring.

Pressure Casting. The pressure-casting technique, although originally developed for glass-polyester materials, is now primarily used for forming metal fiber-reinforced epoxy resins. As mentioned before, it is relatively new, and thus is not as yet widely used. Because of its promise, more space is devoted to it here than warranted strictly on the basis of its extent of commercial use.

A solid hemp-reinforced plaster mold is made from the die model by standard solid plaster casting techniques. It should be kept in mind that for metal fiber-reinforced castings the mold must withstand 300 to 400 psi pressures during the casting operation.

A reinforced wood or aluminum mold box extension is then constructed around the mold to hold the fibers in place. Because of the high compression ratio or bulk factor (as high as 11:1) of the metal fibers, a "fiber reservoir" must be provided above the mold to hold the fibers before compression. For metal fibers, this mold box extension should be 3 to 4 times the depth of the desired cast.

After the mold face has been properly treated with sealant and parting compound, a gel coat of heat resistant epoxy resin is brushed on the mold face to a thickness of 1/16 to 1/8 inch. Before this gel coat becomes tacky, short, 1/16 to 1/4-in.-long aluminum, steel, or molybdenum fibers are flocked onto the gel coat. For small dies, quart-sized flocking guns are available; if both large and small dies are contemplated, metal fiber-flocking guns specifically designed for this use are recommended. The gel coat with the flocked short fibers is then allowed to become tacky.

A preweighed resin mix containing some presaturated metal fibers is then loaded into the mold, followed by a load of preweighed dry metal fibers, which overflows the mold and fills the mold box extension. The metal fibers should be distributed carefully to provide uniform density over the contours of the die, since very little, if any, lateral fiber movement occurs under pressure.

A pressure plug (e.g., hardwood) is constructed, with appropriate vents, to fit over the metal fiber load in the mold box extension, forming in effect a closed mold system. The mold is then closed slowly, allowing the resin to flow uniformly through the fibers. Any excess resin is vented through the holes in the pressure plug. Using a standard hydraulic press or hydraulic jack, a pressure of 200 to 300 psi is applied to the mold and maintained until the exotherm developed sets the casting. This may require anywhere from 4 to 12 hr. Molds should then be postcured, usually for several hours at 300°F, for optimum properties. Time and temperature of cure depend on size of tool and type of resin.

In making matched tooling, the female can be cast in a similar way using the male punch as the mold (or vice versa), with suitable allowance for metal part thickness.

In pressure casting glass fiber-filled epoxy, techniques are similar to those used with metal fiber reinforcements. The gel coat and metal fiber flocking procedure is the same. However, since the glass fibers have a much lower bulk factor than metal fibers, the mold box extension need only be about ½ the depth of the cast. Also, the glass fibers must be presaturated with an equal weight of the resin system under nominal pressure prior to loading into the mold. Using a solid pressure plug, casting is carried out at pressures of about 50 to 100 psi, followed by the same curing cycle.

In fabricating both the metal and glass fiber-reinforced casting, a presaturated ⅛-in. densified metal fiber mat or preform may reduce both pressure and mold box extension requirements. In pressure casting the glass fiber-filled material, use of another preimpregnated metal fiber mat on top of the glass filled charge will provide a much more machinable back to the die. Data on performance of such tools are given in the chapters on specific tools.

Vacuum Casting. Another approach being studied is the use of vacuum casting rather than pressure. According to A. Juras of Metal Fibers Inc., it involves preparing the mold with suitable vacuum holes, filling the mold box with metal fibers and metallic powder, and casting the resin on top of an enclosing perforated metal plate. The vacuum is said to draw the resin and powder down into the fibrous mass, insuring complete and consistent impregnation of the mass.

Cores and Supporting Structures

All the fabricating techniques described thus far, with the exception of mass gravity and pressure casting, are essentially methods of producing a tooling surface. Virtually all tooling surfaces require some type of core or supporting structures. As outlined by Hankins,[2] such cores may serve one or more of the following functions: (1) provide a means of locating the tool in or onto a press or fixture, (2) establish a level tool base, (3) provide a dimensionally stable support for the working surface of the tool, (4) supply the weight required in certain metal-forming tools, e.g., drop-hammer punches, and/or (5) provide additional strength and rigidity to the tool.

Selection of the proper core construction should be made only after careful analysis of the requirements of a particular tool. For example, if a jig or fixture is to be handled frequently during production, light weight is important. If a tool is to be stressed only in certain areas, core constructions can be selected which provide reinforcements primarily in those areas of high stress. If a tool is to be primarily stationary, the cost of lightweight structural reinforcement may be unnecessary, and the most economical solution may be lowest cost solid metal, concrete, or aggregate cores. These and other considerations must be evaluated in each specific case.

Aggregate Cores. Aggregate cores can provide the lowest cost core available. Essentially they consist of a liquid casting resin filled with any of a variety of aggregates. Epoxy or phenolic casting resins can be used. Aggregates may be sand, gravel, volcanic rock, shale, aluminum shot, walnut shells, or a variety of other bulk materials. Approximate maximum loading rates of various aggregates and resin are shown in Table 7.2.

TABLE 7.2. TYPICAL AGGREGATE TYPES AND LOADINGS

Aggregate	Approximate Maximum Loading (pbw Aggregate/pbw Resin)
Sand	10/1
Gravel	12/1
Volcanic rock (expanded)	10/1
Shale (expanded)	10/1
Aluminum shot	8/1
Walnut shells (crushed)	3/1

Source: Hankins.[2]

Major characteristics of aggregate cores include low labor cost, low-to-moderate material cost per cubic inch of cavity, high rigidity, and low-to-moderate strength. They are usually quite heavy.

Aggregate cores have been used primarily in stretch-forming dies, duplicate die models, foundry tools and design study prototypes. More recently aggregate cores with carefully controlled aggregate-binder ratios have been used in drop hammer dies. In stretch dies, the volume to be filled is usually large, and the high cost of epoxies coupled with their exotherm characteristics have required the use of low resin-to-aggregate ratios. Of course, at such low resin contents strengths are relatively low.

The high impact loading encountered by foundry patterns and drop hammer dies requires a higher resin content. Using walnut shell aggregate, ratios of ½ to 1 part by weight of aggregate to resin have been successful. Where machinability is required, of course, mineral aggregate should be avoided.

Aggregate cores can be either cast in place or prefabricated, depending on the type of tool surface. In the case of laminated tool surfaces, the surface is first laminated to the desired thickness as described in a previous section. The aggregate-resin mix is then blended in a concrete mixer or planetary mixing equipment, such as a Hobart or Champion mixer. The mix is then dumped and tamped, or troweled into the cavity, and allowed to cure.

When a cast tool surface is planned, the aggregate core is precast undersized. After the core has cured, it is suspended in the mold, and the surface is cast as described in the previous section on surface casting.

Plastic Foam Cores. The primary attribute of plastic foam cores is rigidity at low weight, although they do not provide the degree of rigidity that aggregates do. They are used primarily for stretch dies, prototypes and other tools where strength requirements are not extreme. Because of their low strength, foam cores usually require a more rigid tool face, e.g., 2- to 4-in. cast phenolic.

Of the variety of plastics foams available, phenolics are the most widely used for tooling. They are low in cost, and relatively simple to formulate. Epoxy foams can also be used, but they cost more and are more difficult to process. These disadvantages are usually not offset by enough improvements in strength in foam-in-place systems to justify their use. Syntactic foams, formed from phenolic microballoons and a resin binder, provide good compressive strength properties, and are particularly useful where simplified mixing and troweling methods of application are beneficial. Although some property data are given in the chapters on epoxies and phenolics, materials suppliers should be consulted for specific information, as properties vary quite substantially.

Rigid urethane foams would provide exceptionally good core properties, but their cost is still high. They offer the benefits of wide variations in density and strength, and where volume production is anticipated, automatic metering equipment is available.

Plastics foams, like aggregate cores, can be either formed in place or preformed. Forming by foaming in place requires careful consideration of possible effects of expansion pressures and thermal changes during foaming on dimensional integrity of the tool face. In relatively closed systems, where such effects may be dangerous to the successful fabrication of a usable tool, the foams can be prefoamed undersize in a rough mold.

The cured foam core is then suspended in the mold and the tool face cast as shown in Figure 7.3. Where a prefoamed core is to be applied to a laminated tool face, the tool face is laid up in the mold, the core is prefoamed, and a binding layer is cast between the core and the laminated face (as shown in Figure 7.9).

Tubular Core Construction. Tubular constructions may be of metal or reinforced plastic tubing, either of square or round cross section. Important benefits of such constructions include high dimensional stability, low-to-moderate weight (depending on whether plastic or metal tubing is used), and low-to-moderate materials cost per cubic inch of cavity. Labor costs are usually moderate to high, because of the hand fabrication required.

The relative merits of metal *vs.* plastics tubing are debatable. Metal tubing provides a higher degree of rigidity; plastics tubing provides lighter weight. Welded metal tubing must be normalized, and dimensional problems may arise in service because of the difference in thermal expansion characteristics between the metal structure and the plastic surface. The importance of such problems depends on the type of tool, dimensional accuracy required, and magnitude of anticipated ambient temperature differences.

The coefficient of expansion of plastics is considerably higher than that of metals, for example, as pointed out by B. Sokol, of Grumman, a typical structural steel has an expansivity of about $7 \times 10^{-6}/°F$, compared with about $30 \times 10^{-6}/°F$ for a cast epoxy. Consequently, for every degree of temperature change, a difference of 0.000023 in./in. of length will occur. Considering a temperature change of from 10 to 110°F for tools stored outdoors, the difference in length of a 4-ft-long tool would be 0.110 inch. If the tool were made of a cast epoxy face on a structural steel member, this would virtually guarantee warpage. However, if the plastic material in intimate contact with the steel were a glass reinforced epoxy, very little, if any, distortion would occur because the coefficients are approximately the same ($8 \times 10^{-6}/°F$ for the glass reinforced epoxy).

Plastics tubing for backing structures is available in a variety of forms and in several materials, e.g., glass reinforced epoxy, polyester and phenolic tubing, paper impregnated with phenolic and polyester resins, etc. These are available from formulators and other materials suppliers.

One of the most common methods of constructing supporting structures of metal or plastics tubing is by adhesive bonding with epoxy resin and glass tape or cloth, or with glass-filled putties. Large supporting structures should usually be prefabricated before attaching to the tool surface. Smaller structures can be built up directly against the back of the tool surface. Maximum strength is obtained at tubing joints by wrapping the joint with glass fiber tape or cloth and saturating with epoxy resin. Chopped fiber reinforced epoxy putty or patching compounds are used to build up fillets around joints. Figures 7.6 and 7.7 show common techniques of fabricating such structures.

In square tubing, "T" or "L" joints can be improved by using hardwood blocks which just fit inside the tubing. The blocks, precut to the suitable "T" or "L" shape, should have several cross cuts to provide a mechanical keying action with the resin to improve bond. The blocks are smeared liberally with resin paste, inserted in the tubing as it is joined, and the joint is subsequently wrapped with saturated tape or cloth. Several common techniques for working with such tubing are shown in Figure 7.8.

Prefabricated structures are usually bonded to backs of tool faces with epoxy putty. Where possible, glass cloth tape or strips of cloth should be used to tie in other sections of the structure to the back of the tool face with resin. The more ties or points of bonding, the stronger the tooling structure will be (also, of course, the heavier it will be). A proper compromise should be reached depending on the service requirements of each tool. Several techniques are shown in Figure 7.9.

Egg-Crate Cores. The term "egg-crate structure" refers to a large number of different structures involving a variety of different materials. The main purpose of such cores is to provide a "honeycomb" type of support, resulting in maximum strength and rigidity with the least material. Common materials used for egg-crate cores include wood, glass-reinforced plastic laminates, wood particle board, sheet steel and aluminum, honeycomb sandwich panels, and Kirksite or iron cast in an egg-crate or honeycomb shape. Egg-crate cores can be further supported with aggregate fill or plastic foam in the cavities. Figure 7.10 shows a typical nonmetallic egg-crate structure.

Egg-crate cores are used in almost every type of tool, including master models and gages, auxiliary tools, foundry core boxes and patterns, and drop-hammer dies. Figure 7.11 shows construction of such a core for a master contour fixture.

Fabrication of egg-crate cores involves cutting, fitting and bonding sheet stock on edge as ribs to the back of the tool face, then bonding other tailored sheets as cross members to the ribs. Such structures can also be prefabricated and bonded to the back of a tool surface.

Specific fabrication techniques depend on the material being used to form the egg crate. One of the most common methods is to use a glass-filled epoxy paste to bond cross members together and to fillet the joints.

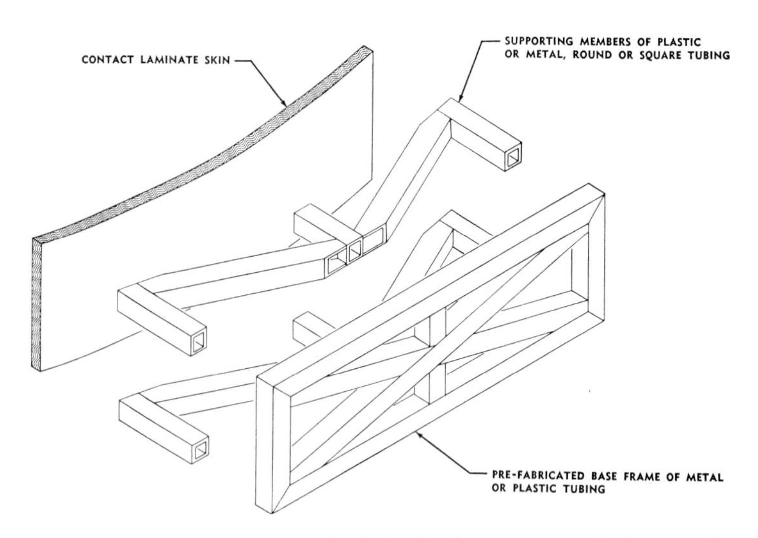

Figure 7.6. Blow up of typical tubular backing structure for laminated tool surfaces. (*Rezolin, Inc.*)

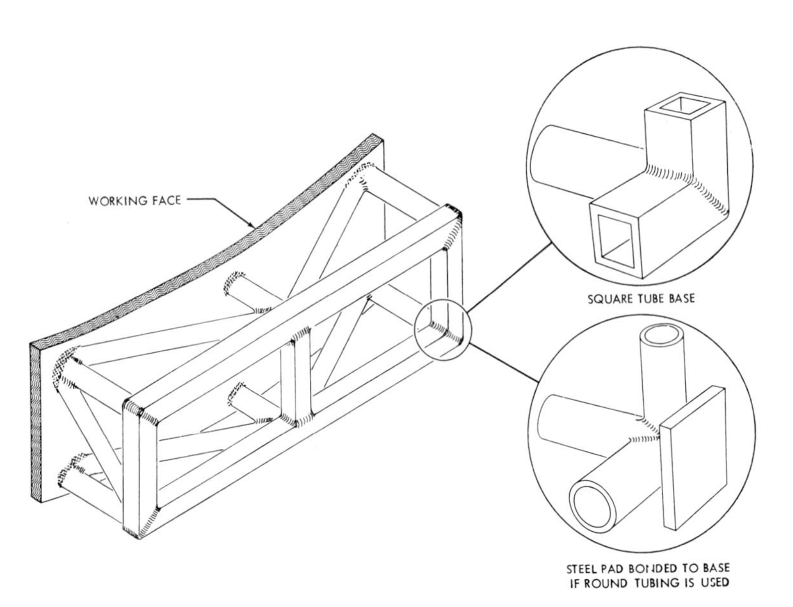

Figure 7.7. Joints may be welded when metal tubing is used, or adhesive bonded with epoxy. If round tubing is used, steel pads can be bonded to provide smooth, stable base. (*Rezolin, Inc.*)

Ultimate strength of such cores, of course, depends on the distance between centers of the ribs and members, the gage and type of material used, and the method and materials used for bonding.

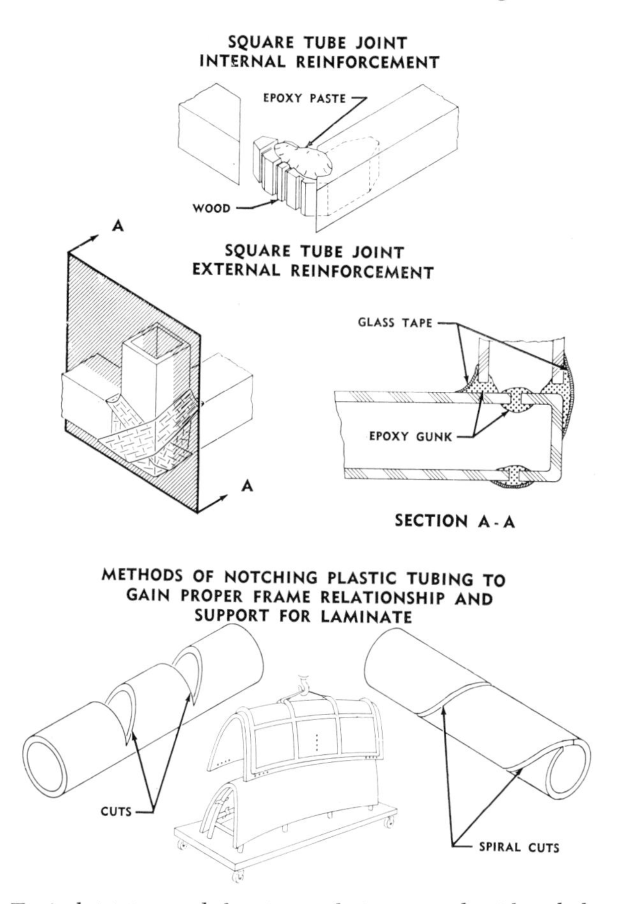

Figure 7.8. Typical joining and forming techniques used with tubular supporting structures. Internal supporting method uses a hardwood block, the external method uses filled epoxy paste or putty, and glass tape saturated with epoxy. Straight and spiral cutting methods, shown at bottom provide tubing with formability required to conform to complex contours, such as that shown in the drill jig. (*Rezolin, Inc.*)

Solid Core. Solid cores are merely masses of material used to fill the cavity of a tool. Although solid cast epoxy or phenolic cores may be used for smaller tools, for larger tools, solid plastic cores are seldom necessary as the strength of such a casting usually exceeds design requirements, and materials costs are high.

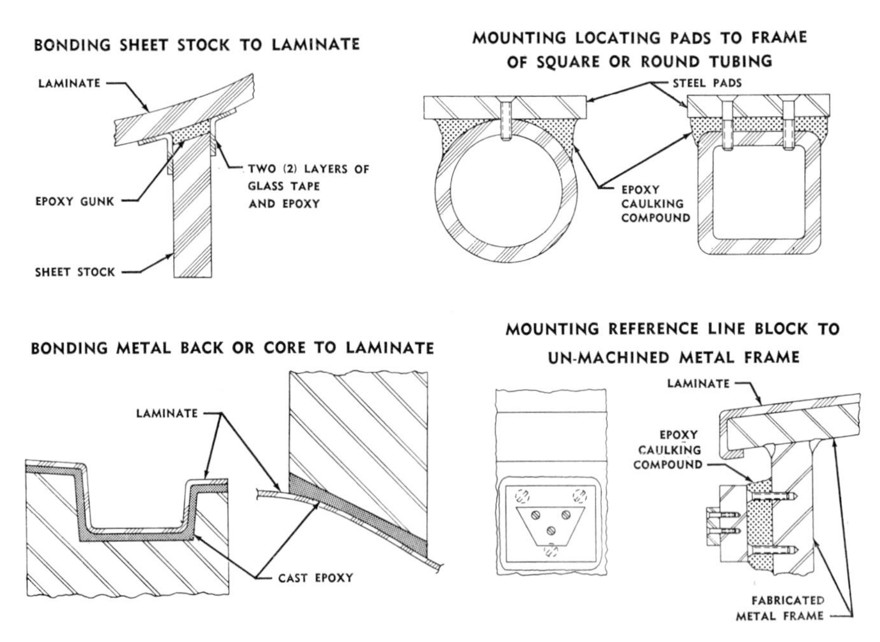

Figure 7.9. Typical techniques for attaching supporting structures to tool surfaces. 1) Technique in upper left is used for bonding cross pieces of egg crate cores to laminate surface. 2) Upper right shows joining of metal locating pads to tubular supporting structure. 3) Lower left shows casting technique used to bond laminate surface to core, in this case metal but could be prefoamed core. 4) Lower right shows method of attaching reference line block to rough metal frame. (*Rezolin, Inc.*)

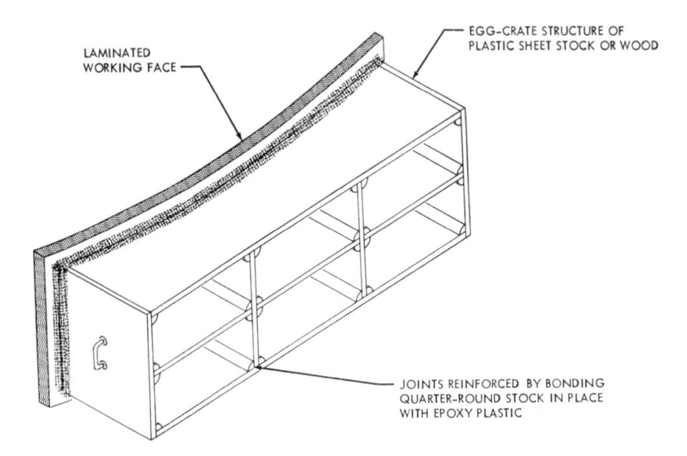

Figure 7.10. Typical nonmetallic egg-crate structure supporting laminated tool surface. (*Rezolin, Inc.*)

Solid cores most commonly used are Kirksite, cast iron or a similar low-cost material. Such cores are inexpensive but heavy, and are used primarily for tools such as drop-hammer dies, or stretch-press dies, where the additional weight is either useful in setting the contour in a metal part being formed, or is unimportant from the standpoint of tool portability.

(*Rezolin, Inc.*)

Figure 7.11. Egg crate core construction for a master contour fixture.

The most common method of producing a tool with a solid core is by the surface-casting technique described before. Or, where a laminated tool surface is required, the laminate is first built up in the mold, then the core is suspended in the mold and resin is cast to form an adhesive layer between the back of the laminate and the core.

Honeycomb Fabrication

The honeycomb materials are described in Chapter 6. Use of such materials in tooling is relatively new. Fabricating techniques vary widely, and depend primarily on the imagination and ingenuity of the tool fabricator or designer.

One of the most promising uses for honeycomb is to replace a number of plies in a laminated tool surface. A fabrication technique used successfully by Convair (and shown in Figure 7.12) is as follows:

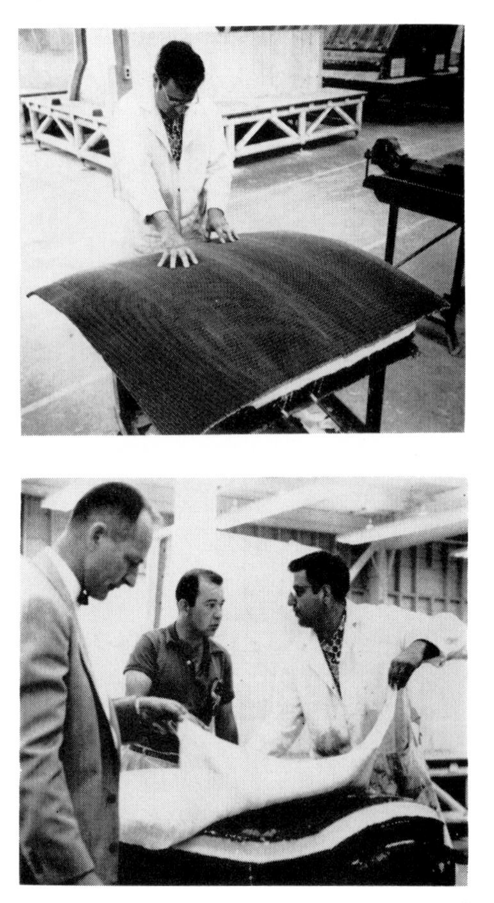

(*Narmco Resins & Coatings Co.*)

Figure 7.12. Convair uses three layers of glass cloth-epoxy on both sides of aluminum honeycomb material (Multiwave) to form tool surface. An egg-crate structure made of honeycomb adds structural support to light weight, durable tool.

First a gel coat and the first three layers of glass cloth laminate are built up using the conventional hand lay-up technique. After the third layer of cloth is applied and saturated with resin, it is trimmed and a final heavy layer of resin is applied. Aluminum honeycomb core material is then draped over the tool and pressed down into the wet resin. After a brief cure, excess honeycomb material is trimmed. Then three plies of glass cloth are laminated to the back of the honeycomb core material.

After the final heavy resin coat is applied, an egg-crate backing struc-

Figure 7.12. (*cont'd*)

ture cut from honeycomb sandwich material is fabricated against the back of the tool. Such fabrication eliminates the time taken to lay up a number of plies of cloth and resin, and reduces the over-all weight of the tool.

To date, most successful use of honeycomb for tools has been in jigs, fixtures and other types of auxiliary tooling. There appears to be no reason why, with careful engineering, the materials cannot offer as great a benefit in other types of tools.

(*Oye*)

Figure 7.13. Caulking between backing material and mold to provide a narrow tool surface is shown here as it is done at Douglas Aircraft Co.

Caulking

Although the term "caulking" can be used to refer to any technique of filling a crack or corner with material, e.g., use of fiber-filled putties or pastes to fillet a corner, the term as used here refers to a fairly new procedure. This involves the application of a thixotropic epoxy resin between a mold surface and a back-up structure. The objective is thus the same as that of surface casting.

The technique requires a special compound that can be used in a caulking gun or extruder. If large amounts of the material are to be used, it is mixed, placed in polyethylene tubes and stored under refrigeration until used.

The preparation of the mold or model and the core or back-up are the same as previously described for surface casting. But the technique is primarily suitable for applying a relatively narrow tool surface. The resin is applied from the caulking gun in the same way that a seam is caulked. Typical technique is shown in Figure 7.13. The technique has been used effectively for facing large hold-down fixtures, as a filleting material for wood foundry patterns, and as a solder material for various applications.

Planning

Before fabricating a tool, careful thought should be given to the type of tool, its requirements, and the best method of fabricating a tool to meet these requirements. This section on pre-fabrication planning is adapted from an excellent summary by Weaver [4] of Naugatuck Chemical. Although his summary specifically applies to molds for reinforced plastics parts, his basic approach is valid for all types of plastics tools.

Given an acceptable design, a tested prototype, and an engineer familiar with plastics fabrication, a number of steps should be taken in laying the groundwork for a successful tool. Where several molds are required, a pattern must be made, then a master mold, then a mold master from which the production molds can be fabricated. Before beginning any of these steps several questions should be answered to determine how many fabrication steps must actually be taken, and what is the best method for each step.

In determining what steps to take, the following type of questions should be answered:

1. Will one mold suffice to produce the required units in the given time?
2. Was a full-scale model made for approval and testing? If so, can it be used as a pattern? And can it be used for more than one mold?
3. What is the best approach from the pattern-making standpoint?
4. What part requirements will determine how the mold is to be made?
5. Consider the production process carefully: For example, if the tool is a mold for molding a reinforced plastic part, can molding operations be simplified? Or can some assembly operations be eliminated by combining parts in a larger tool?
6. What is the best type of fabrication to provide optimum strength and stability?

Most molds will be a result of the best over-all compromise, determined by detailing as many fine points as possible. Weaver indicates the following points as details to be considered both in pattern making and determining part and production requirements:

1. Pattern making:
   a. Should the mold be made in one piece? Should it be male or female?
   b. Is the symmetry of the part such that only half a pattern will suffice?
   c. Has sufficient design attention been given to run-off required, sufficient radii, undercuts, part thickness, clearances, and tolerances?
   d. What are surface finish requirements?
2. Part requirements:
   a. Must the part be one-piece? Or where two or more parts are required, where are seams or joints least objectionable, or where can they be used to advantage?
   b. Can the mold be made in several parts to suit molding or assembly convenience?
   c. Is the part to be refinished, or used as-molded?
3. Production requirements (for molds for reinforced plastics parts only):
   a. Can the mold be used advantageously as a jig?
   b. Could a simple, inexpensive jig release a mold to production?
   c. Should the molds be stationary or movable?
   d. Can staging or platforms be eliminated by a split mold?
   e. Would it be advantageous to eliminate costly jigs and fixtures at the expense of a more expensive molding operation?
   f. Can standard width materials be used to best advantage?
   g. Are all portions of the mold easily accessible for hand lay up techniques?

The answers to these questions provide a good picture of what is to be done, and permit a relatively accurate cost estimate of the tool.

Production Controls. Careful planning is only as effective as the degree to which it is put into practice. The hand work involved in fabricating a tool, and the nature of plastic materials require close quality and production controls.

After production plans are complete, confer with the persons responsible for each major step in the production operation, and go over exactly what is to be done, how it is to be done, and who is to do it. From this conference, a check list and schedule of operations should be developed, coupled with a *realistic* time schedule. Such a check list and schedule can preclude many of the mistakes which often result in either an unusable tool, or costly rework and refinishing of the tool. Some of the more prevalent errors, their cause, and corrective procedures are outlined in Chapter 8.

Weaver gives a typical molding check list as follows (specific check lists, or course, depend on the type of tool, and the materials and constructions used):

1. Materials of construction
   a. Parting agent.
   b. Overlay, or gel coat, catalyst or hardener, promoter, diluents and fillers.
   c. Resin type, catalyst or hardener, promoter, diluents and fillers.
   d. Reinforcements, type, size, and finish.
   e. Bracing and framing materials.
2. Reinforcement preparation
   a. Provide cutting list and patterns where necessary.
   b. Stack cut patterns on hand trucks or skids after coding so that they may be removed in order of lay-up.
3. Method of lay-up
   a. Application of parting agent.
      1) Number of coats.
      2) How it is to be applied.
   b. Application of overlay or gel coat.
      1) Number of applications and time between.
      2) Formula for each application.
      3) Time to be allowed before lay-up is begun.
   c. Lay-up
      1) Lay-up list showing location of patterns, coding, etc. Cutting list can be used.
      2) List resin formulations. Use master batches wherever possible.
      3) Give amount of resin mix required per ply or pattern depending on method of application.
      4) Where required, provide a graph or table of catalyst per pound of resin mix versus temperature to give required gel time.
4. Bracing
   a. Provide diagram of exact location and type of bracing.
   b. Describe method of attachment to mold.
   c. Have bracing units prefabricated and preassembled wherever possible.

5. Additional information—In each of the above items, the following can also be listed:

a. Equipment required in type and number.

b. Men required and time allowed for each step.

c. Defects or things to watch for and the suitable corrective measures to be taken.

REFERENCES

1. Eldred, D., "Sprayed Reinforced Plastics," *Product Engineering* (Feb. 8, 1960).
2. Hankins, N. K., "Core Structures For Plastics Tooling," paper presented at the 14th Annual Meeting of the Reinforced Plastics Div., The Society of the Plastics Industry, Inc., Feb. 1959.
3. Oye, L. F., "Fabrication of Plastics Tools," paper presented at the 25th Anniversary Meeting of the American Society of Tool Engineers, March 1957.
4. Weaver, E. P., "Large Reinforced Plastics Molds," paper presented at the 16th Annual Technical Conference, The Society of Plastics Engineers, Jan. 1960.
5. Young, M. K., "Tooling with Gypsum Plasters for Reinforced Plastics," paper presented at the 10th Annual Meeting of the Reinforced Plastics Div., The Society of the Plastics Industry, Inc., Feb. 1955.

8. *Tool Modification and Repair*

The processibility of plastics makes modification and repair of plastics tools a relatively simple, inexpensive process, as compared with that of metal tooling. Frequently such alteration of hard tooling is not practical because of the cost, or because of warpage or distortion which may occur when metal is welded.

From the standpoint of the work to be performed, the question of whether the work is a modification or a repair is not important. From the cost accounting standpoint it is. Reworking a plastic tool may be (1) a modification of the tool to permit it to do the same job more efficiently, to perform an additional job, a lesser job, or to perform an entirely different job, or (2) repair of the tool to correct faulty fabrication or failure of the tool to do its specified job.

Typical examples of common modifications include:

1. *Addition modification* such as: (a) more hole locations for a drill rack, (b) additional location points on a checking fixture, or (c) lengthening of a routing fixture to accommodate a longer part.
2. *Subtraction modification,* such as: (a) reducing number of hole locations in a drill rack, (b) removing trap beads from a drop hammer die, or (c) shortening a trim template to accommodate a shorter part.
3. *Change of tool function,* such as (a) altering a hand routing template to become a spot welding fixture, or (b) altering a checking fixture to become an assembly fixture.

When tool modification is required, the economics of modifying the existing tool versus replacing the tool completely should be considered carefully. In general, as pointed out by Sokol,[1] subtraction modification is relatively inexpensive and simple. On the other hand, addition modification or change of tool function modifications are more difficult and expensive.

In deciding whether to modify or replace a tool, the considerations are the same as those involved in deciding whether to repair a damaged tool or replace it with a new tool. Consequently, the following discussion of repair versus replacement generally holds true in considering modifications.

REPAIR VERSUS REPLACEMENT

Sokol [1] classifies economics and degree of urgency as the two factors that determine whether a tool should be repaired or replaced.

Economics

Economic considerations include (1) estimates of cost of repair both in materials and labor, (2) the number of parts yet to be made on the tool, (3) the original or replacement cost of the tool, and (4) the chances of the repair being successful.

Although repair and revision of plastic tools are relatively inexpensive, the initial cost of the tools is usually much lower than that of metal tools. Consequently, in many cases where metal tool repair would be mandatory because of the high replacement cost, it may be actually cheaper to replace a plastic tool than repair it.

The number of parts yet to be made on the tool often determines the type of repair. If only a few parts are to be made, a "quick and dirty" repair may suffice. If several thousand more parts must be made, the repair must be more carefully made and thus becomes more expensive.

With the proper materials and fabrication techniques most repairs can be successful. Repairs may occasionally fail in impact type tools such as drop hammers, or tools subjected to high loads, such as metal draw dies. In any case, the possibility of failure of a repair should be considered in estimating costs.

Urgency

Just how quickly a damaged tool must get back into production often affects choice of the method of repair. The necessity for getting the tool back into production immediately may force the tool engineer to use the quickest rather than the most economical or successful method.

Often the part being made on the plastic tool is critical to an assembly and may hold up an entire production line. Unfortunately, in these cases the fastest repair is the most economical. Tool engineers should insist where possible on sufficient time to adequately plan and accomplish a repair. Rushing a repair job frequently results in unsatisfactory repair, and an additional waste of time in the long run.

Evaluating the Damage

Failures in a plastic tool should be carefully evaluated to determine the cause. Simple repair of failures caused by basic errors in design, will only result in repetition of the same failures. In general, failures may be caused by (1) improper design, e.g., insufficient support in areas of excessive load, (2) improper or faulty fabrication techniques, e.g., entrapped air bubbles in laminated tool face, (3) mishandling, e.g., dropping a checking fixture on the floor, or (4) normal failure at end of anticipated tool life.

A general rule, applicable to virtually all repairs, is to always use a material which will provide the same or better physical properties than the original material in the tool. In repairing metal-forming tools, hardness of the cured material is critical. It must be precisely the same as that of the original plastic material so that the metal part formed by the tool will not be marked at the repair interface.

A variety of techniques can be used in repairing plastic tools. Obviously details of all possible methods cannot be given here. However, the following outlines typical tool failures, their probable causes, and specific repair methods as suggested by Sokol [1] and Weaver.[2] Of course, specific requirements of a tool may often call for modifications of these techniques, or use of entirely different methods.

SURFACE IMPERFECTIONS

Many minor imperfections may appear on the surface of a plastics tool. Occurrence of such imperfections, the repair of which may require only a sanding operation, immediately reduces the benefits inherent in plastics tooling. Such imperfections, and their general causes include:

1. Rippled or uneven appearance—Pattern not splined or sanded sufficiently or properly.
2. Rough surface, with the appearance of wood grain, minor indentations, etc.—Pattern not polished sufficiently or surface improperly prepared. Or, parting film or agent has not been properly applied, dust or dirt was on the surface before application of gel coat or overlay.
3. Regular lines at periodic intervals—Station marks in the pattern not removed, or the pressure of braces causing raised areas in the mold.

4. Pattern transfer—Application of first plies of glass too soon after application of gel coat or overlay, or too thin gel coat or overlay.

5. Surface pitting—Mixing resin too rapidly or careless application of surface coat, or moisture in the plaster mold.

Repair Methods

The extent of surface repair depends on the requirements of the tool. The alternatives are sanding and filling, or complete roughing up and refacing of the tool surface. Sokol [1] recommends complete replacement if the surface contains more than 5 pits/sq inch. If such pitting exists in one area it probably exists throughout. Tapping the surface lightly with a ball peen hammer will show up such faulty areas.

Surface Replacement. Where the entire surface or a substantial area of the tool surface is to be replaced, the following procedure is usually satisfactory:

1. On a cast surface sand the faulty tool face (No. 60 grit should be satisfactory) to remove a fairly uniform layer. In laminated tools, strip off one or two surface layers of cloth instead of sanding.
2. Prepare the mold surface against which the face is to be formed in the same manner conventional plaster or wood molds are prepared, i.e., dry, and apply parting compound.
3. Brush on surface coat of resin and dust with a nylon flocking. After surface coat gels blow off excess flock.
4. Apply one or two layers of glass fabric (150, 164 or equivalent) with a suitable laminating resin to the surface coat resin. Dust with flock unless continuing immediately.
5. Liberally apply thixotropic laminating resin to both the roughened tool face and to the laminated surface. If the tool is a thin-walled laminate, perforate the body laminate with a pattern of $\frac{3}{16}$-in. holes to allow for air bleed.
6. Mush the roughened tool face into the new face by making contact first at one side of the tool and then progressing slowly toward the other, forcing out air and excess resin.
7. Allow resin to cure, trim off excess resin and clean up tool.

A repair as outlined above is expensive, but effective. Application of the surface laminate (step 4) may be eliminated, but use of the laminate prevents subsequent breaking through the surface coat to any small air bubbles retained in the interface between the new surface and the body of the tool.

Localized Repair. Complete resurfacing is rarely necessary. The more common failure is surface break-through by relatively large air bubbles in a few localized areas. Repair of such failures is relatively quick and easy.

1. Voids should be cleaned and opened up slightly with a rotary file.
2. A thixotropic surface coat resin should be probed into the prepared voids, leaving an excess above the tool face.
3. After cure, excess resin is filed down to the level of surrounding tool surface.

SURFACE CRUSHING

The cause of surface crushing in a plastics tool must be carefully determined. Probable causes include (a) excessive local loading on the tool, (b) improper mixing of the original tooling compound, or (c) air bubbles trapped a short distance below the surface resin. Voids or air bubbles may be caused during tool fabrication by the resin gelling too quickly and preventing air from working out of the material; or the resin may not have been sufficiently thixotropic, allowing too much run off; or, high exotherm may have caused "blowing" of resin.

Repair Methods

Repair of crushed areas caused by air bubbles or voids is similar to that described for surface imperfections.

If tool failure in operation is due to a general lack of compressive strength of the material in the tool, possibly the tool should not be made of that plastic material, and the tool should be replaced. If the failure is due to faulty design of the tool, modification may be feasible to reinforce the weak area.

Where crushing is caused by high local loading, such as wrinkles in sheet metal being drawn in dies, the repair may consist of insertion of a metal plate. The following procedure can be followed:

1. Grind out the crushed area slightly beyond the limits of damage.
2. Prepare a piece of $\frac{1}{4}$-in. steel, properly shaped, by welding several short steel bolts to its sand-blasted rear side and shaping the face to conform to the area in which it is to be located. The bolts help key the steel into the plastic.
3. Brush a casting resin in the ground-out hole and on the underside of the steel plate.
4. Suspend the steel insert properly over the cavity and pour the balance of the resin between the insert and the tool to fix the insert in place.

If a local crushing is caused by carelessness such as dropping a heavy weight on the tool surface, the repair is simple and can be accomplished in the same way as that described above for localized repair.

FRACTURES (CRACKS OR CHIPS)

Probable causes of fractures in tools include:

1. Improper design of the tool—Design should be carefully evaluated to determine whether modification is feasible, or whether metal tooling should be substituted.
2. Overloading the tool—A set of dies designed to form 0.032-in. SO aluminum should not be expected to form 0.064-in. half hard stainless steel.
3. Mishandling the tool—No tool is designed to be driven over with a fork truck.
4. Differential thermal expansion—Large differences in expansivity between plastics and metal back-up structures may cause plastics surfaces of plastics-capped metal tools to crack. This is a particular problem with tools stored outdoors in areas where ambient temperatures change radically. This seldom occurs where outdoor temperatures remain upward of room temperature; it may occur often where temperatures go below freezing. In such cases, cracking can be prevented during the construction of the tool by applying a heavy brush coat of a flexible resin between the plastics cap and metal supporting structure.

It is very important that plastics tools stored outdoors should be brought to room temperature before put in use. A cold (0°F) plastics drop-hammer die will shatter like glass if operated cold.

5. Poor weathering characteristics—Certain plastics weather poorly, particularly when exposed to sunlight. Where cracking is due to weathering and tools must be stored outdoors, tools should not usually be repaired, as such repairs can only be temporary at best.

Repair Methods

Chips and cracks can usually be effectively repaired by filling with casting resin. The following procedure is typical:

1. Tool is washed down with solvent to remove oil and grime from fractured area.
2. Cracked area is opened up and ground out with a rotary file.

3. Cracked area is dammed up with masking tape, and a clay dam built up to form a sprue.
4. Epoxy resin is mixed and poured into sprue to completely fill cracked area.
5. After cure of the resin, the tape and clay are removed, excess resin filed off, and the tool returned to service.

Another successful method is to apply an epoxy paste or putty and work it well down into the crack with a putty knife or trowel.

WARPAGE

Warpage of a plastic tool after fabrication can be a critical and costly problem; this is particularly true when warpage occurs well along in the life of the tool. If the tool has been used in production for several months, for example, the cost of reworking the tool is compounded by the production of faulty parts or other tools from the warped tool.

Probable causes of warpage include (1) improper fabrication, such as not normalizing welded steel supporting structures; or application of too many layers or plies of epoxy glass too rapidly, causing strains to be set up due to high exotherm; or improper cure; (2) creep in the plastics tool; (3) differential thermal expansion coefficients between plastics and metal components; (4) exposure of the tool to excessively high temperatures; (5) overloading the tool, which may be caused by improper supporting structures resulting in excessive point or line stresses; or (6) shrinkage of the resin. According to Sokol,[1] four out of five cases of tool warpage are due to either plastic creep or plastic-to-metal thermal expansion incompatibility.

When creep of the plastics material is found to be the cause of warpage, the tool is usually one made entirely of plastics, and made with too scanty a cross section. In general, a span depth ratio of 8:1 should be held.

Repair Methods

Before repairing a creep-warped tool, the tool should be heated to 40 or 50°F higher than its anticipated highest operating temperature and allowed to cure at that temperature for 6 to 8 hr. This will insure a fully cured material, minimizing tendency to creep. After cooling the tool to room temperature, the repair, which usually consists of a refacing of the working surface, is carried out using the same techniques outlined in the section on refacing pitted surfaces.

When warpage is due to thermal expansion incompatibility between the plastic and metal components of the tool, the tool is usually a total loss.

Shrinkage of the resin is a rare cause of warpage today. Available resins, particularly the medium-high-viscosity epoxies, have a very low degree of shrinkage. Filling the resin or laminating with reinforcements further reduces shrinkage until it is negligible. If warpage should occur due to shrinkage (this usually occurs at the time the tool is removed from its mold) the simplest alternative is to oven-cure the tool, then reface by procedures previously outlined.

A typical example of faulty tool fabrication is described by Sokol.[1] The tool is a trim and contour checking fixture, 4 ft long, 2 ft wide, and 6 in. high, roughly triangular in shape. The body of the tool is steel pipe welded to form a triangular frame. Short steel angles run along the spine of the steel pipe frame and tie into a 1 x ½-in. plastic band that runs around the perimeter of the tool, establishing the contour and trim line of the part.

After a month's service, parts produced with the tool were found to be out of dimension, by the inspection department, which returns the defective tool to the tooling department. Examination shows that the tool is "out" in areas by as much as 0.060 in. The manner in which the plastics strip is warped indicates stress at the points of tie-in with the steel body angles. Discussion with tool shop personnel provides the answer: The welded tubular steel body of the tool was not normalized before tie-in with the plastics face band. Progressive relaxation of the steel warped the tool.

Repairs in this case would consist of: (1) Removal of the plastics face band from the tool and normalizing the tubular steel structure; (2) Laminating a new plastics face band against the master tool; (3) Tying in the plastics to the steel, removal of tool from master, and cleaning up of the tool.

Total cost of rework:

Material	$10.
Labor and Overhead	$112.
Total Cost	$122.

LOOSENING OF COMPONENTS

Small components such as bushings, locating pins, mounting lugs and steel routing edges occasionally come loose from a plastics tool. Repairs are usually accomplished quickly and easily. Probable causes of such failures include (1) improper initial design or mounting of component. (2) misuse of component, or (3) accidental high impact to component.

Repair Methods

If the cause is accidental high impact or misuse that will probably not recur, the surfaces to be rejoined can merely be roughed up and re-bonded with epoxy resin.

However, if the cause of damage is unexpected operating conditions that will continue to exist, the attachment of the component must be re-evaluated and possibly redesigned. Some common problems and their solution are as follows:

1. *Loose bushings.* Metal bushings may come loose for one of three reasons: heat of drilling, impact, or plastic creep due to continued high unit loading.

Where the heat generated by the friction of a rapidly rotating drill and chips causes loosening, the bushing can be coated with a ⅛- to ¼-in. ceramic coating cement and bonded in place with epoxy. For small bushings, an alternative is the use of anchor bushings which are equipped with metal tabs that may be riveted to the body of the tool.

Bushings with hexagonal or square midsections for mounting are available and will alleviate the problem of loosening by unexpected impact.

When a bushing is heavily loaded in one direction for a long period of time, the surrounding plastic material may creep and the bushing loosen. Beefing up the area surrounding such bushings to provide a better load distribution will prevent loosening.

2. *Locating pins.* Fixed locating pins that must be replaced due to breakage, bending or other reasons are handled in much the same way as bushings. Pins should have flared or knurled areas to provide a mechanical key in the plastic tool.

3. *Mounting lugs and steel edges.* Metal lugs or edges should always be provided with a mechanical key to improve adhesion to the plastic. Mere plastic-metal adhesion should not be expected to hold such parts in position during tough service. Metal parts should be roughened by sand blasting or other means. Also, internal mechanical keying or external machine screws should be used.

WORN AREAS

All tools are subject to wear, metal-forming tools particularly so. Normal wear is always nonuniform in nature. Certain areas wear away more rapidly than others depending on the type of tool and its use. For example, in draw dies, the radii suffer first while in drop-hammer dies, areas coming in contact with the edge of the sheet metal and wrinkles in the sheet metal wear first.

Occasionally certain areas of a tool are abnormally worn due to misuse, e.g., gouges caused by prying formed metal parts from the die with a screwdriver.

When a tool is worn excessively in certain areas, careful consideration should be given to the cause, and whether the tool should be repaired or modified. In a great many cases, an area of a tool wears excessively because it should not be made of plastics at all; a metal insert should have been used in the first place. Unfortunately, too often, the tool engineer considering plastics tooling thinks the greatest economies are obtained by making the entire tool of plastics. Actually, the optimum benefits are obtained by only using plastic in those areas of the tool where their properties are sufficient. In areas of high wear, a metal insert should be used.

Where wear occurs in a number of areas on the tool, indicating that the tool is reaching (or has reached) the end of its useful service life, the question of repair versus replacement is critical. Worn areas can be effectively repaired by techniques described previously, but the cost of such repairs versus the cost of an entirely new tool must be carefully compared.

REFERENCES

1. Sokol, B., "Repair and Modification of Plastic Tools," paper presented at the 25th Anniversary Meeting, American Society of Tool Engineers, Mar. 1957.
2. Weaver, E. P., "Large Reinforced Plastic Molds," paper presented at the 16th Annual Technical Conference, Society of Plastics Engineers, Jan. 1960.

9. *Some Tips on Plastics Tool Design*

DONALD SONCRANT, CHIEF ENGINEER

Modern Pattern & Plastics, Inc.

The designer of plastics tooling must be a capable tool designer who understands the processes, the machines, the materials being worked, and the environmental conditions likely to be encountered. The construction of plastics tools frequently involves standard tool-making methods, with only some of the working surfaces being made of plastics. In fact, a plastics tool may often look just like any conventional tool, since only the materials of construction have changed, not the function of the tool nor the machine in which the tool is to be used.

Broad design generalizations are difficult to make. A full understanding of the capabilities of plastics materials is a prerequisite to effective design. However, there are a number of specific recommendations which can be made to help realize the fullest potential of plastics as a tooling material.

Tips to Reduce Costs

Probably one of the most common reasons for using plastics in tools is to reduce the cost of the tool. The following recommendations can frequently help reduce costs to a minimum:

1. *Simplify tool design.* A tool design consisting of word descriptions and sketches in conjunction with the part print eliminates the need for a complicated, completely dimensioned drawing, and may be the first step toward cost reduction.

For example, drill jigs made of glass-reinforced plastics laminates and used to drill holes in shaped sheet metal parts are frequently made from a sample part which has the holes drilled in their correct location. Directions for such a tool might consist of a free-hand sketch, or markings on the part itself with a written description specifying laminate thickness and the size and type of drill bushings required.

2. *Use existing models or parts.* Since plastics is essentially a duplicating material, a shape must always be present, except in special cases such as loft template constructions. Whenever possible, use a shape already available, such as a model or a prototype part, and reproduce this shape in plastics.

3. *Build new models to male shape.* When master models have to be made, build them in a manner easiest to duplicate (usually a male shape), and to the side-of-metal that requires the least amount of transference of part thickness.

4. *Use flat run-outs.* Flat run-outs are easiest to build, and should be used wherever possible.

5. *Eliminate undercuts and loose pieces.* Remember that in reproducing a shape in plastics, the plastics shape must be removed from the model. Wherever possible, eliminate all undercuts and loose pieces, simplifying shape reproduction.

6. *Use lattice-type laminates.* Lattice-type laminate structures should be used wherever possible instead of solid structures. Lattice structures require less material and less labor, and are lighter in weight.

7. *Select supporting structures carefully.* Each type of supporting structure has benefits for specific types of tools. Wood is fast and lowest in cost, but has relatively poor dimensional stability, and well-defined planes of weakness. Cast iron is next to wood in cost and is readily available in terms of delivery time, but it may require time-consuming, costly machining. Cast aluminum is more costly than iron but usually can be obtained more rapidly, and is more rapidly machinable. Cast steel is most expensive and takes longer to get, but offers maximum strength. Weldments are nearly as expensive and as strong as cast steel, and can be obtained sooner. Fabricated plastics supporting structures can be costly, both in terms of materials and labor, but offer low weight.

8. *Use fillers in plastics tooling materials.* Where relatively large masses of plastics are required and strengths are not critical, fillers can increase the yield of the relatively expensive plastics materials.

9. *Pot large flat tool areas.* Slow expensive machining of large areas can be eliminated by potting surfaces from a surface plate to pads, ribs, or whole continuous surfaces.

Utilizing Properties of Plastics

Alteration and Repair Capability. In many initial tool designs there are general areas where modification or alteration of design may be necessary in the future. Where possible, these areas of plastics should be made so that changes can be made simply by grinding, sanding, or machining, or by patch and repair techniques.

High Strength/Weight Ratio. Where tool weight must be minimized, the high strength-to-weight ratios of plastics should be used to the fullest. To obtain the lightest possible tool, each component must be stressed to its safe limit. Any unnecessary lamination or thickness only tends to increase weight. A properly designed plastic fixture should weigh, at most, ⅓ as much as a comparable steel fixture.

The designer should calculate stresses in all components and specify the reinforcement that will give the most strength in the direction required with the least weight, rather than the usual practice of specifying a standard thickness throughout. Reinforcement here means both reinforcement such as glass cloth or metal fibers, and supporting structures of plastics or metal tubing. Plastics are used at stress levels nearer the upper limit of their physical strengths. This is not as true of metals, so it becomes clear that such stress analysis is even more critical in plastics than metals.

Also, the published strengths of plastics laminates and castings are obtained on standard specimens made under ideal conditions and with ideal materials in a laboratory. Such conditions are not likely to be encountered in a tool shop. Consequently adequate safety factors should be provided.

Soft Surfaces. Although the softness of plastics is a limitation in terms of resistance to wear and abrasion, it can be of benefit in providing a soft surface on which to rest polished parts or other parts where nicks or scratches would be detrimental. In such cases, double gel coats should be used to preclude reinforcement or filler "show-through"; or a resilient or flexible material may be specified.

On the other hand, where the surface must be resistant to wear or abrasion, either abrasion-resistant surface formulations should be used, or metal inserts incorporated. Where metal inserts are used, they should be carefully anchored to preclude loosening.

Corrosion Resistance. The resistance of plastics to chemicals and other types of corrodants can be an important consideration where tools are to come in contact with such materials as corrosive greases and cutting oils. In such cases, plastics tubular supporting structures should be used, rather than wooden bucks or steel weldments.

Heat Resistance. Heating of a tool may be caused by (1) applied heat, either ambient, or external heat applied to perform an operation, (2) heat from the material, which may be residual heat from a previous forming operation, exothermic heat from the material in the tool, or heat caused by cold-working of the metal being formed, or (3) friction, caused either by rubbing of a cutting tool on guides or the work piece, or movement of the work piece over the plastic surface.

The determination of just how hot the plastic may become before it degrades or loses strength is extremely difficult. As mentioned elsewhere, heat distortion temperature is only an arbitrary value, indicating the temperature at which a standard specimen deflects an arbitrary degree under either of two standard loads (i.e., 264 or 66 psi). But the value can be used both as a general comparison between two plastic materials, and as an indication of the general temperature range at which the plastic loses a degree of its strength.

Temperature build-ups in specific areas of a plastics tool can be prevented either by insulating the plastic from heat or by conducting it from the plastic. Methods of doing this are discussed elsewhere.

Tips on Metal-Plastics Joining

In all cases where plastics are joined to metals by forming the plastics against the metal and curing, the metal should be thoroughly cleaned and roughened to provide a mechanical lock. Even when this is done, provisions should be made (e.g., use of undercuts) to keep the plastics under compression, rather than allowing primary shearing stresses to act on the plastics-metal interface.

Where a laminate surface conforms to a contour of a metal supporting structure, radii should be kept at a maximum. Glass fabrics when stressed tend to straighten out, and if radii are too small, the laminate will pull away from the metal at the corners.

For joining plastics to metal where frequent disassembly or removal is planned, use (1) through-bolts and nuts, although flanges on the plastics must be strong enough to withstand stresses imposed; (2) embedded nuts in the plastic material; or (3) such devices as Heli-Coil inserts, which are highly satisfactory.

10. *Metal-Forming Tools*

Plastics tools in the metal-forming category include (1) all tools used to form sheet metal by direct contact between the metal and the plastics tool face, as well as (2) tools in which plastics are used to accurately locate and hold metal components which actually perform the metal working operation. The first type of tools includes draw, restrike, stretch-form, Hydropress, and drop-hammer dies; the second type includes flange, and trim and pierce dies.

The use of plastics for short-run metal-forming tools has been one of the most widely publicized applications for plastics tooling. But in addition to some outstanding successes, there have been some outstanding failures.

Linzell of Chrysler points out that possibly one of the greatest problems in plastics tooling is that the tool engineer may assume that if he is going to make a plastics tool, the entire tool must be made of plastic. Often the most successful use of plastics may be only in one member of a two-member tool, or as a facing material for a metal core. For example, in some cases, plastics will fail when used for both male and female members of a matched draw die, but will perform satisfactorily if used for only the female or male member.

Plastics metal-forming tools are primarily suited for short-run production. Success is now being achieved for some types of parts in medium-run production, but the applications must be chosen with care.

Use of Plastics

The question of when and where to use plastics for metal-forming tools cannot be answered categorically. The answer depends on a variety of specific factors dependent on the requirements of the tool. However, Esdale [3] outlines a number of questions, the answers to which may give you a better idea of whether plastics should be used for your particular job.

As a general rule, Esdale points out that since metal dies have a longer life than plastics dies, where only straight machining on a planer or milling machine is required to form the surface of a die and its binder line, conventional materials such as iron or steel should probably be used. However, where irregular surfaces or contours must be duplicated in the die, punch and binder line, plastics should be considered.

For such applications, consider:

1. How many pieces are to be formed?
2. How soon is the first piece needed? How soon are the others needed?
3. How much work must the die accomplish? And to what tolerances?
4. What is the end product; e.g., is good appearance essential?
5. Does the design of the stamping readily lend itself to the use of plastics for building the die?
6. Are metal machining facilities available, along with sufficient skilled craftsmen familiar with fitting and barbering metal, or must some easier method of die construction be followed to get acceptable stampings?
7. Would the severity of the draw require multiple metal inserts in the ring, pad or punch?
8. How much capital is available for the die construction program?

Primary Advantages. Lower costs and shorter lead times are the primary benefits of plastics metal-forming tools. Initial tooling costs are usually an important factor in determining economical production volume for a given part; consequently tooling costs affect permissible frequency of economical design changes. Reducing tooling costs 30 to 70 per cent provides much more rapid amortization of tools, and thus substantially reduces the volume of parts required to justify tooling.

Ease of repair of plastics tools is also of benefit, both in maintaining production with minimum press down-time, and in making a design change. As detailed in Chapter 8, design modification, such as eliminating style lines or adding style lines, can often be accomplished rapidly and economically without producing an entirely new tool.

The lead time required between tool design and production can be drastically reduced (by months in some cases) by forming the plastic tool to the required shape in one operation, eliminating time-consuming (and costly) spotting and finishing steps required for most hard tooling.

The speed of fabrication of plastics tools can also be utilized for temporary or emergency production. When production volume warrants the fabrication of metal tooling, but the tool delivery date is several months off, plastics tools can be fabricated rapidly to produce parts until the arrival of the metal tools. Plastics tools can then be stored until the metal tools need repair or replacement. They can be used as replacement dies until the metal tools are repaired or replaced, minimizing press down-time and loss of production.

Limitations of Plastics for Metal Forming. As mentioned before, plastics behave differently than metals. They will never completely replace, only complement, metal tooling. An analysis of external stresss which will act on the tool will indicate quite clearly whether a plastics die will work in a given metal-forming operation. These stresses are determined by the type and gage of metal being formed, the degree to which it must be deformed plastically, and the rate at which it is formed. Other factors affecting a plastics die are the heat generated in the metal by the forming operation, friction between the moving metal and the plastic tool face, and the type of finish on the metal.

Weaver[7] points out that the science of pressed metal is not exact. Experience, perhaps more than theory, must be used to design successful tools. Exact stresses which will be set up in an untried stamping are impossible to determine. But approximate loads required to draw given gages of a given metal to certain depths can be calculated. A comparison of these forces with the physical limits of plastics materials should provide a guide to the expected die life. Following is a discussion of several of the problem areas in the use of plastics for metal-forming tools, as outlined by Weaver.

Draw radii are a primary source of concern, since maximum loads occur in such areas. Failure at such radii is usually caused by a combination of excessive compressive, shear and frictional forces. Tests on cold-rolled steel, 16 gage and greater, have shown conclusively that draw radii of from 3 to 5 times the metal thickness are required for best results. Production runs of parts incorporating such radii in volumes of 1000 parts or more normally require metal inserts.

Heat generated during metal forming is a prominent factor limiting die life. In draws of extreme area reduction and fast metal displacement, the heat generated by realignment of grain structure within the metal can exceed the maximum useful temperature of the plastic material. The extremely low thermal conductivity of plastics limits such generated heat to the die surface, and continued operation leads to rapid failure with marked surface galling.

Resilient plastics facing materials have relatively high impact strength, but surprisingly low fatigue strength. Consequently, such dies are not usually recommended for ironing and spanking operations. Also, once a wrinkle has formed in the metal stamping, a plastic die will be of little value in eliminating the wrinkle by spanking or bottoming. The plastics will usually deform to conform to the wrinkle. Once such deformation occurs, the tool will fail rapidly. Consequently, the formation of a wrinkle should be a danger signal. Metal inserts should be located in such areas. Often complete elimination of wrinkles is not economically feasible or possible with existing part design.

Excessive burrs on metal blanks can provide severe galling of plastics tools. Plastics die rings are usually undesirable even for low-volume production. Tensile strength and hardness are not high enough to withstand the repeated shearing action of a burr.

Metal blanks should be clean. The relative softness of plastics will often cause pick-up of foreign material from the metal surface. Plastics with a Shore hardness of less than D85 will invariably pick up material from dirty blanks.

In selecting a plastics material, remember that some forms of abrasive fillers will definitely "mark off" drawn panels, particularly panels made of polished stainless steel and aluminum. Dies for aircraft parts or decorative parts should use fillers of a size and hardness which will not deface the drawn panels.

Materials and Methods

Epoxy resins are the most widely used materials for plastic metal-forming tools. Construction techniques vary widely depending on the specific tool needs and the approach of the tool maker. With the basic fabricating techniques described in Chapter 7, the tool engineer should use his knowledge of the stress requirements of his tool, as well as some imagination, in selecting the proper fabrication technique.

Both laminated and cast tool faces are used. Laminated surfaces are more costly and take longer to fabricate, but they provide maximum strength and dimensional stability. Cast tool surfaces are more quickly fabricated and thus should be used if they can meet mechanical requirements of the tool.

Cores or backings for tool surfaces may be of cast epoxy or phenolic (often filled with aggregate), Kirksite, iron or steel which has been rough-cast solid or in an egg-crate configuration, or phenolic or epoxy foams where stress requirements permit and light weight is important.

When using foamed or cast plastics cores, prefabricating the core is reported to provide the higher degree of accuracy. Casting or foaming in place in the mold, against the back of the tool surface, is quicker and more economical and affords sufficient accuracy for many types of tools.

Metal powder-filled epoxy putties or pastes have been used both for surfacing of dies, and for the entire die, where the die is relatively small. For example, some of the most successful applications of such materials have been in relatively small male dies for such forming processes as Hydroforming, Marforming, and rubber-pad forming. Common fabrication techniques involve troweling face coats on a mold, followed by conventional resin casting techniques.

In conjunction with the newer technique of reinforcing the tool surface with metal fibers, the pressure casting of metal fiber-reinforced high-temperature epoxy core structures is highly promising.

Although materials and construction methods differ radically, the following is a brief run-down of some of the most common techniques used for various types of tools.

Draw Dies. Most commercial draw dies today are made by surface-casting epoxy resin, or laminating epoxy resin, on a metal core, although in some cases, one of the members may be all plastic. Weight is not usually critical in such tools, and using plastics-capped metal cores combines the low cost, rapid duplication of surface contour obtainable in surface casting or laminating techniques with the low materials cost of metal in the massive part of the tool. The flow chart in Figure 10.1, Steps 1-13, shows a typical method of producing such a surface cast die, from the initial die model to the final completed die.

All-plastics draw dies can be successful but the loads to be imposed on the tool during the forming operation must be carefully analyzed to determine whether plastic will suffice. Often the compromise will be to produce one die member, such as the punch, entirely of plastics, while the other member is metal, or plastics-capped metal. When the second die member is all metal, the metal die surface can be used (with wax placed to allow for metal thickness) to form the mating plastics punch surface.

Where the mating die is to be plastics-faced, probably the most common fabrication technique is the use of a $\frac{1}{4}$ to $\frac{1}{2}$ in. laminated epoxy die surface, with a solid epoxy or phenolic core cast through an attached base plate. Such core resins can be filled to reduce cost. After the resin in one member is cured, sheet wax or "Celastic" can be used to provide for metal thickness before casting or laminating the mating die member.

In some cases binder rings can also be of plastics or plastics-faced, but they should only be used on simple draws, and for limited production. Conventional metal rings should be used if production is not extremely limited, or when deep draws or severely abrasive conditions are encountered.

A substantial amount of time and effort have been spent on making use of metal fiber-reinforced epoxies for draw dies. The bulk of the dies

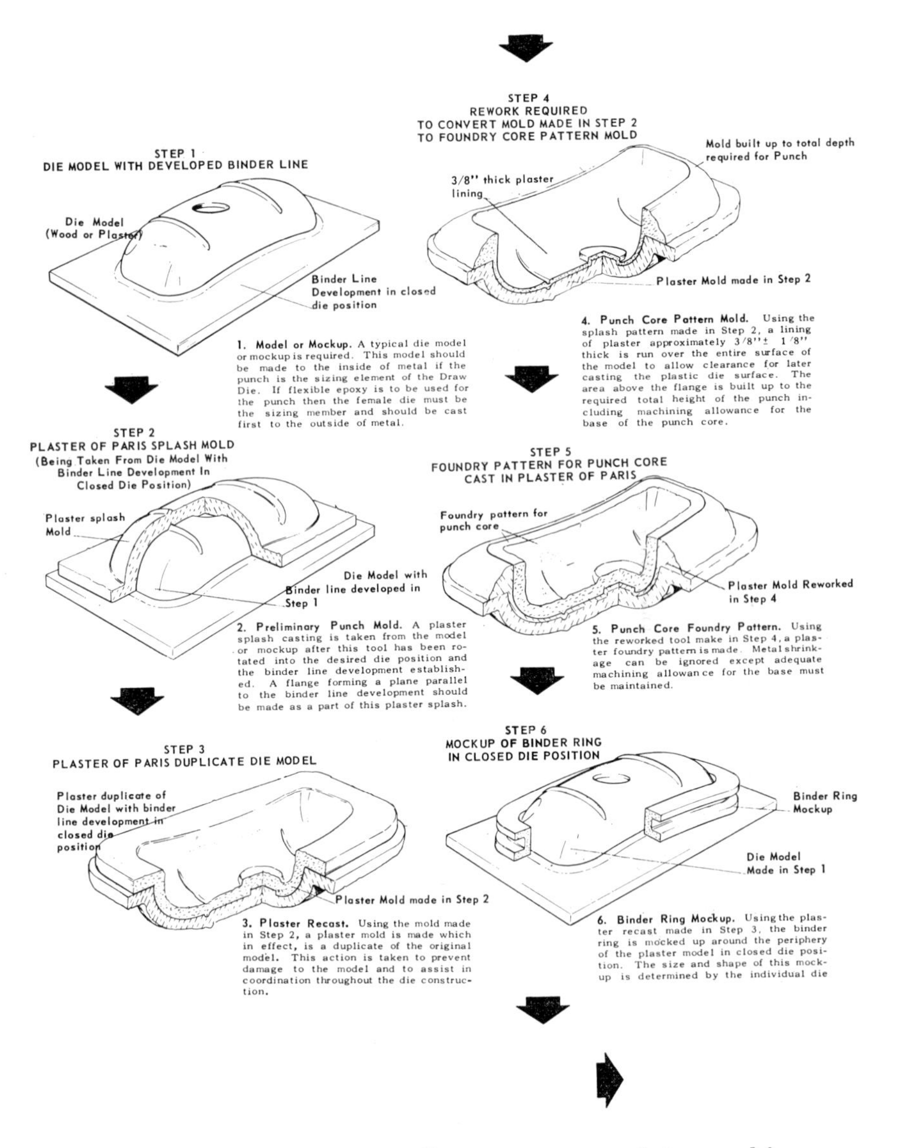

Figure 10.1. Steps 1 through 13 illustrate a common technique used for building epoxy-surfaced metal-draw dies. (*Rezolin, Inc.*)

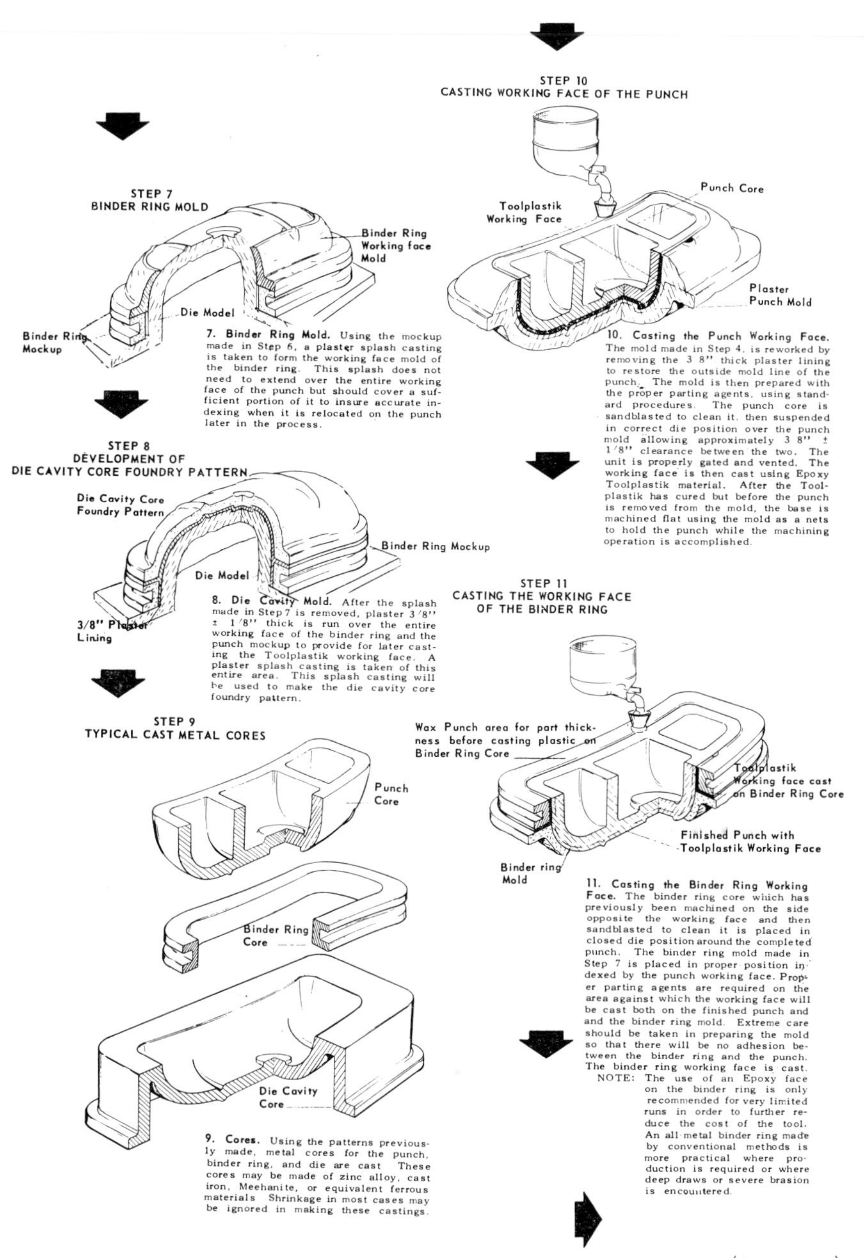

7. Binder Ring Mold. Using the mockup made in Step 6, a plaster splash casting is taken to form the working face mold of the binder ring. This splash does not need to extend over the entire working face of the punch but should cover a sufficient portion of it to insure accurate indexing when it is relocated on the punch later in the process.

8. Die Cavity Mold. After the splash made in Step 7 is removed, plaster 3/8" ± 1/8" thick is run over the entire working face of the binder ring and the punch mockup to provide for later casting the Toolplastik working face. A plaster splash casting is taken of this entire area. This splash casting will be used to make the die cavity core foundry pattern.

9. Cores. Using the patterns previously made, metal cores for the punch, binder ring, and die are cast. These cores may be made of zinc alloy, cast iron, Meehanite, or equivalent ferrous materials. Shrinkage in most cases may be ignored in making these castings.

10. Casting the Punch Working Face. The mold made in Step 4, is reworked by removing the 3/8" thick plaster lining to restore the outside mold line of the punch. The mold is then prepared with the proper parting agents, using standard procedures. The punch core is sandblasted to clean it, then suspended in correct die position over the punch mold allowing approximately 3/8" ± 1/8" clearance between the two. The unit is properly gated and vented. The working face is then cast using Epoxy Toolplastik material. After the Toolplastik has cured but before the punch is removed from the mold, the base is machined flat using the mold as a nets to hold the punch while the machining operation is accomplished.

11. Casting the Binder Ring Working Face. The binder ring core which has previously been machined on the side opposite the working face and then sandblasted to clean it is placed in closed die position around the completed punch. The binder ring mold made in Step 7 is placed in proper position indexed by the punch working face. Proper parting agents are required on the area against which the working face will be cast both on the finished punch and and the binder ring mold. Extreme care should be taken in preparing the mold so that there will be no adhesion between the binder ring and the punch. The binder ring working face is cast.

NOTE: The use of an Epoxy face on the binder ring is only recommended for very limited runs in order to further reduce the cost of the tool. An all metal binder ring made by conventional methods is more practical where production is required or where deep draws or severe brasion is encountered.

(*turn page*)

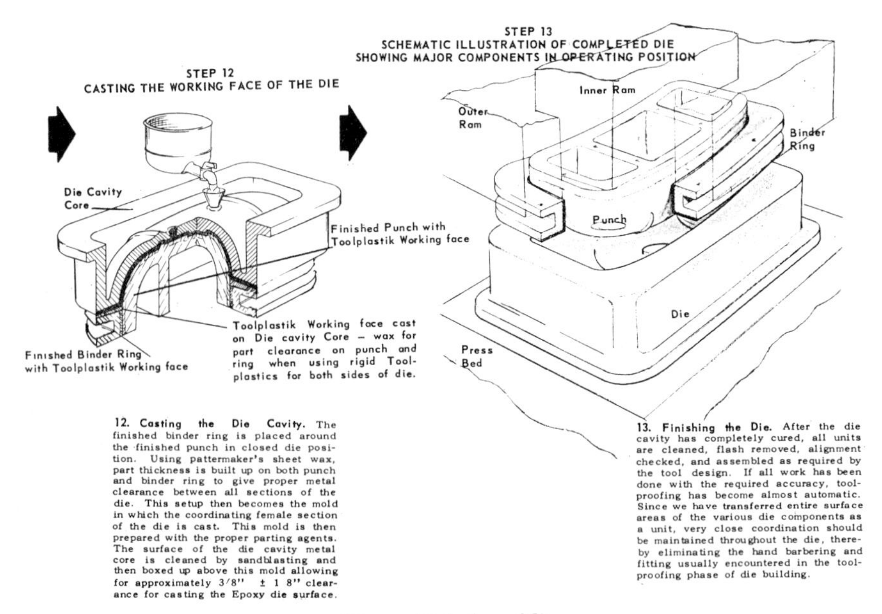

12. Casting the Die Cavity. The finished binder ring is placed around the finished punch in closed die position. Using pattermaker's sheet wax, part thickness is built up on both punch and binder ring to give proper metal clearance between all sections of the die. This setup then becomes the mold in which the coordinating female section of the die is cast. This mold is then prepared with the proper parting agents. The surface of the die cavity metal core is cleaned by sandblasting and then boxed up above this mold allowing for approximately 3/8" ± 1 8" clearance for casting the Epoxy die surface.

13. Finishing the Die. After the die cavity has completely cured, all units are cleaned, flash removed, alignment checked, and assembled as required by the tool design. If all work has been done with the required accuracy, toolproofing has become almost automatic. Since we have transferred entire surface areas of the various die components as a unit, very close coordination should be maintained throughout the die, thereby eliminating the hand barbering and fitting usually encountered in the toolproofing phase of die building.

Figure 10.1. (*cont'd*)

made by this technique utilize metal fiber-flocked surfaces and the pressure-casting technique, and have been highly successful. Their accomplishments are itemized in detail in a subsequent discussion of tool life.

Drop Hammers. The most common technique using plastics in drop hammers is to surface-cast a rigid (Shore D85-90 hardness) epoxy face on a metal core. According to Delmonte,[2] materials with hardness of D55-60 should be used for forming steel; D45-50 for aluminum. Where radii are relatively large and contour changes are gradual, the resilient facing for the punch may be cast against the rigid epoxy die with no allowance for metal thickness. However, where punches incorporate abrupt changes in dimensions and sharp radii, wax or other provisions for metal thickness should usually be made prior to casting the matching die member.

All-plastics drop-hammer dies have been constructed and used successfully. The most recent technique developed at Rohr Aircraft involves the use of an epoxy laminate over a cast epoxy aggregate core. The aggregate core (walnut shell filler) is cast in the die mold after first laying up the laminate surface.

When plastics cores are used, a steel frame around the die members will help the tool withstand the high bursting stresses normally associated with drop-hammer dies. Such a frame also helps in clamping the tool to the hammer bed. Where additional weight is required to set radii in the metal part, lead can be cast into the core. In producing such a core the aggregate or casting resin mix is poured to about 1 in. of the top of the mold. After cure, lead is cast into the mold to fill the cavity in the back of the core.

(*Shell Chemical Corp.*)

Figure 10.2. Where a reinforced plastic facing is required for a metal draw die, lay up the laminate on the properly prepared mold. Then, as shown in this picture of the operation at Allite Div., Allied Products, clay locating ridges can be applied to hold the metal core exactly ½ in. away from the surface. Epoxy casting resin is then poured into the ½ in. area, bonding the metal core to the laminated epoxy tool surface.

Stretch Dies. A common technique in fabricating stretch blocks where weight is no consideration is the use of a concrete core, with a cast epoxy face. For such constructions, the concrete is cast undersized and the cured surface degreased. An appropriate amount of liquid epoxy is then poured into the mold, and the concrete core is lowered into the liquid mix, forcing the resin out to fill the void between mold and core.

Where light weight is important, stretch blocks can be constructed of a laminated epoxy surface, backed with a low-density core. In some cases, a foam plastic core will be sufficient. More commonly, an egg-crate core is constructed, using any of a variety of materials as discussed in Chapter

7. The cavities in the core structure can then be filled with a foam-in-place phenolic foam. Suitable back and support should be provided, such as a "T-" or "I"-beam steel structure.

Where a low-weight egg crate-supported stretch block is planned, splining techniques can be used eliminating the need for conventional master molds. Loft templates are constructed and set up on a steel base

(*Ren Plastics, Inc.*)

Figure 10.3. Floor pan is one of 10 major body panels drawn by Checker Motors on epoxy dies. Both the lower die and punch are epoxy faced, backed with metal cores.

plate or framework. The templates can be rigidly supported near their outer contours by reinforced plastics or metal tubing. Metal mesh or glass cloth is then spread between the templates and attached near their outer contours. A filled epoxy core resin is spread on the mesh and allowed to gel (usually 6 to 8 hr). An epoxy splining paste is then applied, screeded to the contours of the templates, and cured. If additional support is required, the cavities in the egg-crate core can be filled with aggregate or plastic foam.

Plastics Pads. Plastics pads, spotting racks and stripper pads often provide cost benefits in conjunction with metal-trim, pierce-and-blank, steel-rule, and restrike dies. Although metal is used in such tools for either the shearing action or to provide the fine detail required, plastics, in the form of reinforced laminates, paste or castings, can provide the dimensional stability, accuracy and strength to locate and hold such metal members, or to hold parts, or to strip parts from dies.

Multistage Forming Operations. Actually, plastics, when properly used, can contribute to virtually all of the tools used in many multistage forming operations. For example, Weaver [8] describes tools used to produce 50,000 panels. The panels required a number of forming operations, including blanking, drawing, trimming, flanging, piercing and restriking.

A steel rule blanking die uses a metal fiber board impregnated with epoxy resin to locate and hold the steel rules securely in place.

The matched draw die is constructed by the pressure-casting technique using a steel and molybdenum fiber-reinforced high-temperature epoxy surface, backed with glass fiber-reinforced high-temperature epoxy core. The ring is cast Meehanite, and the dies are mounted on boiler plate shoes.

Redraw dies consist of metal fiber-reinforced epoxy surface and glass-reinforced epoxy in the punch. The lower ring is cast "Meehanite." The upper ring is of metal fiber-reinforced epoxy. The stripper pad is faced with a laminate of room temperature-cured epoxy, bonded to a cast iron core with cast epoxy.

In the pierce-and-blank die, room-temperature-curing epoxy laminates backed with an iron casting provide the contoured punch and pad. Here the function of the punch and pad is only to hold the panel in its proper position during the piercing and flanging operation. Contoured tool steel die inserts perform the actual piercing and flanging operation.

On the final restrikes and flange operations, since radii are of metal thickness dimensions and definition of character lines is important to the finished panel, plastics are not used on the die surfaces. However, cast epoxy spotting racks are used as tool aids to assure accurate positioning of the panels.

Tool Life

For the most part, metal-forming tools must withstand relatively high stresses in service; consequently they must be carefully designed and fabricated to use plastics materials properly. Because requirements for each metal-forming operation differ there is no definitive set of rules by which die life can be accurately predicted.

Life of a die will depend on the type, gage and condition of the metal being formed, the shape of the final part (i.e., the degree of working involved), and the type of forming operation. In general, plastics are well accepted for development dies involving 1 to 20 stampings and prototype draw dies involving possibly 1 to 500 stampings. They have limited use in short-run production of 500 to 10,000 stampings. Several successful uses are reported in medium-production dies involving 10,000 to 50,000 stampings. Isolated cases have been reported in medium-high-production dies for 50,000 to 100,000 parts, and in high-production dies for quantities above 100,000 parts.

In prototype and development dies, difficult parts involving deep draws with relatively heavy metals can be accomplished. In low-production dies the type of part and material to be formed must be determined by experience. In medium-production quantities (10,000 to 50,000 stampings) contoured punches and pads, where suitable, usually require metal rings and inserts. Plastics dies for higher production quantities are generally limited to the easily formed metals, making use of large radii, metal rings and metal inserts.

Sheet metals succesfully formed on plastic dies include aluminum, stainless steels, cold-rolled carbon steels, copper alloys, and others. Of course, thickness of metal depends on the design factors, such as depth of draw and draw radius. Following are specific examples of successful dies, including types and thickness of metal formed and draw radii.

Pressure-Cast Dies

With the metal fiber-reinforced epoxy pressure-cast draw dies, some useful initial estimates have been developed to indicate their practical utility range. According to Mazzucchelli,[4] these estimates are as follows:

1. Dies will produce 50,000 or more stampings of such metals as 0.025-in. brass if bead radii are 1/16 in. or more, or 1/2 in. or more where radii are very highly stressed. Metal inserts should be used on parts with sharper radii. Such dies hold a screw-fastened insert satisfactorily, and with less mark-off than found with standard epoxies.
2. Dies will produce 1000 stampings of 0.038-in. cold-rolled steel with draw depths up to 2 1/2 in., if a draw radius increase from 1/8 to 1/4 in. is accepted. They will reproduce 30,000 or more of such stampings with an increase of 1/8 to 1/2 inch.
3. Dies will produce 1000 stampings of 0.029-in. cold-rolled steel drawn over a 1/32-in. radius to a 1-in. depth of draw and maintain radii sharper than 1/8 in. For any stampings above this range at least one blank-holder surface should be of metal.
4. For prototype work in deep drawing 0.050 in. heavy cold-rolled steel, for a draw depth of 5 1/2 in. draw radius will increase from 1/8 to 1/4 in. after 300 stampings; from 1/8 to 1/2 in. after 700 stampings.

5. Dies will draw aluminum without scratching. Metal fiber-epoxy is superior to glass-polyester for draw rings on prototype dies.

6. A confidential program involving 35 such dies has demonstrated that they can satisfactorily draw 3/16-in. stainless steel prototype panels over a ½-in. radius to a depth of about 18 inches. Boiler-plate draw radius inserts were used in some of the most critical dies in otherwise complete mass cast dies weighing as must as 7500 lb.

In considering the above initial evaluations, remember that the work was carried out during a time when tooling techniques for the pressure casting type of construction were still being evolved and improved.

Other Dies

Because results of use of plastics metal-forming tools are highly dependent on the specific job, the following case histories of successful dies provide an indication of what such tools can and cannot do.

1. *Draw die* (3/8-in. cast epoxy face; Kirksite core): Cold-rolled steel, 18 or 20 gage, is drawn to a depth of 8 in. to form ambulance roofs measuring 68 x 159 in. Richard Bros. Division of Allied Products draws about 4000 such roofs annually for Miller-Meteor Co. Over-all cost reduction compared with Kirksite dies is about 10 per cent, primarily through 50 per cent reduction in spotting time. Additional benefits result from ease of replacement of worn surfaces as they occur.

2. *Drop-hammer die* (laminated epoxy face on both punch and die; cast walnut-shell-filled epoxy core): Savings of upward of $90/cu ft in manufacturing costs resulted from Rohr Aircraft's switching from epoxy-faced metal drop hammer dies to all epoxy dies. Their technique was unusual in that both die and punch faces were laminated, and with rigid epoxy rather than resilient types. Also, during fabrication of the punch, the approximately 50-50 walnut shell-resin casting mix is poured to within about 1 in. of filling the cavity. After the punch is installed in the hammer, this void is filled with molten lead to provide weight.

Rohr has found the dies highly successful for forming contoured and beaded skins, contoured and angled "Z's" and shallow pans of 2024-0, 7075-0, and 6061-W aluminum; Types 302, 321 and 347 annealed stainless steels; and 1010 and 1025 steels.

3. *Draw dies* (flocked metal fiber-epoxy face; pressure-cast metal-fiber reinforced epoxy core): Punch and pad, both made of steel fiber-reinforced epoxy, were used by Long Manufacturing Div., Borg-Warner Corp., to produce radiator tank-tops of 0.025-in. brass. Tanks were about

23 x 4 x 7 in. deep. Plastic dies cost $2225, compared with $3000 to $5500 for equivalent steel tooling, as estimated by independent die shops.

Production dies were built with a steel trim-line flange and a metal ring insert on top to form the radiator filler neck. Dies were still in operation after producing over 130,000 parts; length and width remained un-

(*Ren Plastics, Inc.*)

Figure 10.4. Cold-rolled steel ambulance roof, described in text, stamped by an epoxy-faced metal punch by Richard Brothers Div., Allied Products Corp. Production is 4000 roofs annually.

changed, as did the 1.9-in. punch radius. After 50,000 stampings, the reinforcing rib radii increased from 0.045 to 0.060 in. at the top of the punch, and from 0.19 to 0.50 in. at the curved lower ends. These curved ends represented 5 per cent of the bead area and were in highly stressed locations on vertical side walls. These changes did not affect performance of stampings, and there was no loosening of the metal insert in the punch.

4. *Draw dies* (steel fiber-reinforced pressure-cast inserts): Four steel fiber-reinforced epoxy punch and pad inserts were used for a first draw and a redraw die with metal rings to produce a refrigerator bottom panel

for Hotpoint. The cost of each of the plastic-inserted dies was $275 less than the all-metal dies; delivery was made in 5 weeks versus 9 to 15 weeks required for equivalent all-metal dies.

The 16 x 21 in. plastic inserts have formed 125,000 panels of 0.036 cold-rolled steel. No repairs were required, and the contoured punch inserts remained relatively unchanged. The greatest change occurred due to wear in a sharp radius of the plastic insert of the redraw die, which

(*Furane Plastics, Inc.*)

Figure 10.5. All-plastic drop hammer dies—an unusual technique described in text—are used by Rohr Aircraft to form a wide variety of metals.

was really an extension of the metal radius. The radius started at 0.08 in., increased to 0.19 in. after 5000 panels, and extended to 0.44 in. after 15,000 panels. It remained unchanged during subsequent production. The increase still met requirements for the panel.

5. *Draw dies* (steel fiber-reinforced epoxy punch, steel fiber-reinforced surface with glass fiber-reinforced pressure-cast core die and ring): Dies are used to form 21 x 27 x 1 in. deep charcoal-broiler tray of 0.029-in. cold-rolled steel. These produced 1000 parts; draw radius increased from 0.031 to 0.11. Dies were modified to provide metal plate draw radius insert.

6. *Draw dies* (steel fiber-reinforced epoxy punch and upper ring; Ampco-bronze inserts in glass-reinforced polyester in lower ring): Aircraft housing 28 x 15 x 3½ in. deep in 0.040 in. aluminum was still running after 500 stampings. Performance indicated no need for bronze inserts if

steel fiber-reinforced epoxy had been used in lower ring. The aluminum was not scratched.

7. *Draw dies* (steel fiber-reinforced epoxy face; steel fiber-reinforced epoxy pressure-cast core on both punch and pad): Dies produced an aircraft reinforcing section 4 x 10 x ½ in. deep in 0.045 stainless steel in quantities of 200 parts. The draw radius of 0.37 in. remained unchanged; 0.05-in. radius ends increased to 0.18 in., and required metal inserts.

8. *Radial forming die* (steel fiber-reinforced epoxy on aluminum core): Die forms stringer "Z" section 40 x 2½ in. in 0.032-in. stainless steel. It was still running after 80 parts with no difficulty.

Explosive Forming Dies

The future of plastics molds or dies for explosive forming of metals is questionable. Some tooling people feel that the degree of use will be negligible; others are highly optimistic, based on initial evaluation. Probably the major problem in determining how extensively they will be used is the state of the high-energy-rate-forming art. Explosive and other high-energy-rate forming methods are still relatively new in terms of widespread commercial practicality. Techniques have not been fully developed as yet. Because there has been some successful work in applying plastics tooling techniques to explosive forming, this section will briefly summarize the results which have been reported.

Essentially, explosive forming is a method of utilizing the high and virtually instantaneous pressures generated by explosion to form metal at high speeds. Certain metals, such as titanium, "Inconel," "René 41," "Hastelloy X," and types 321 and 17-7 stainless steels are difficult to form cold. But when deformed at high energy rates (500 to 21,000 ft/sec versus 2¼ ft/sec for conventional drawing presses; 26 ft/sec for drop hammer forming) a substantial amount of plastic deformation can be produced without occurrence of the usual work-hardening phenomenon, which produces increased hardness and reduced ductility. Such techniques often eliminate a number of intermediate drawing steps interspersed with annealing.

Also, explosive forming produces such shapes as spheres, cones, bulged tubes, cylinders and corrugated panels at lower cost, in less time, and at closer tolerances (no spring-back problem) than usually feasible with other techniques. Obviously, interest in such techniques is high.

Although there are several methods of high-energy-rate forming, the type for which most work has been done in investigating the use of plastics molds is explosive forming in a hydraulic medium, such as water.

In this technique, the mold or die, the sheet metal preform or blank, and the explosive charge are immersed in water. The space between the metal preform or blank and the mold is evacuated with a vacuum pump, and the charge is fired. The water transfers the force generated by the expanding gas to the metal part, forcing it to take the shape of the die.

Actually the environment imposed on the die material is not quite as severe as might be imagined. Effective pressure decreases with distance from the charge. For example, North American reports that pellet-shaped charges developing a force of about 2 million psi exert a force of only about 75,000 psi at a distance of 3 ft, 50,000 psi at 3½ ft, and 30,000 psi at about 4 ft from the explosion. Also, according to Savitt,[6] a 0.005-lb. explosive charge used to form a sheet metal blank which was about 1.5 in. from the charge developed on effective force on the blank of only about 30,000 to 50,000 psi. Of course, the problem is to select the proper combination of such variables, as type and size of explosive charge, distance and location of the metal blank, etc., which will provide optimum forming forces on the metal, yet minimum effective pressures on the die.

Also, according to Williams of Rohr, with water as the forming medium, the heat at the die surface only reaches about 900°F., and only for an instant.

Common die materials used for explosive forming have graduated from concrete masses to steel or Kirksite. The benefits obtainable by using plastics for the mold or die surface are the same as those for any plastic metal-forming tool: cost and lead time. Also, a smooth finish on the mold is mandatory since during forming a part will pick up the slightest imperfections on a die surface.

Of the various die constructions possible, glass-epoxy laminate face backed with any of several types of core materials appears to offer the best service at present. A cast face would certainly be less costly, but strengths do not appear to be sufficient. Some work is currently being carried out in evaluating a resilient cast epoxy face.

High-temperature epoxy formulations are laid up with glass cloth in the manner described in Chapter 7. Laminate thickness is determined by the hardness of the metal being formed, the size of the explosive charge required to form it, and the distance from the charge, e.g., aluminum commonly requires a minimum of ⅜ in. thickness; titanium at least 1 in.

Most evaluation work has been done with metal or reinforced concrete back-up for the laminate face. Such constructions are fabricated by conventional techniques.

Ryan Aeronautical is reported to have had excellent results using a cast resilient epoxy core. They claim that such structures minimize die deflection and shock in the production of parts with vertical walls. On an average, their dies are reported to have a compressive strength of 20,000 psi and a tensile strength of 12,000 psi.

All-plastics dies obviously are desirable, as they are reported to reduce manufacturing costs by up to $90/cu ft of tool, and to reduce die weight by at least 75 per cent, compared with concrete or metal-cored dies. But in cases where maximum forming strength is required, plastics must be backed with metal or concrete.

REFERENCES

1. Bryan, B. J., "Epoxy Dies for Explosive Forming," *The Tool Engineer* (Feb. 1960).
2. Delmonte, J., "Drop-Hammer Tools from Epoxies," *Aircraft and Missiles Manufacturing* (Feb. 1959).
3. Esdale, W. J., "How To Choose Plastic Dies," *Automotive Industries* (Aug. 15, 1956).
4. Mazzucchelli, A. P., "New Fiber-Reinforced Epoxy Compositions," paper presented at 13th Annual Conference, Reinforced Plastics Div., The Society of The Plastics Industry, Inc., Feb. 1958.
5. Oye, L. J., "Fabrication of Plastic Tools," paper presented at 25th Anniversary Meeting, American Society of Tool Engineers, Mar. 1957.
6. Savitt, J., "Explosives Form Tubes With and Without Dies," *American Machinist*, (June 15, 1959).
7. Weaver, W., "Known Limitations of Plastics Tooling," paper presented at 25th Meeting, American Society of Tool Engineers, Mar. 1957.
8. Weaver, W., "Production Plastics Dies Up to 50,000 Pieces and The New Pressure Casting Method of Die Making," paper presented at 14th Annual Conference, Reinforced Plastics Div., The Society of The Plastics Industry, Feb. 1959.

11. *Models and Prototypes, and Auxiliary Tooling*

Two groups of tools for which plastics are well accepted, but which are usually treated separately, are models and prototypes, and auxiliary tooling. The two are grouped here because their requirements are usually quite similar: high degree of dimensional accuracy and stability, with load-bearing requirements usually of secondary concern. The group is large, and because strength requirements are usually not high, it represents one of the oldest uses for plastics in tooling.

The two major categories covered here include tools of the following type:

1. *Models and prototypes:* Master patterns or models; duplicate models and prototype parts; die models, try-out dies, and duplicate die models; spotting models; and masters for such operations as pantograph, Keller and electrospark machining.
2. *Auxiliary tooling:* Checking, locating and assembly jigs and fixtures used to provide reference locations for assembly or manufacturing operations, and tools used to aid in inspecting a manufactured or fabricated part during or after completion of the part. Thus, it includes such tools as drill jigs and cages, welding fixtures, router blocks, master gages, contour and trim line checking fixtures, cubing frames and paint spray masks.

Primary Advantages

Accurate, speedy, low-cost reproduction of surface contours and dimensions is the primary benefit of plastics for such tools. For example, a unit of 12 fixtures used as masters for making balloon-type welding fixtures cost $68,000 in steel with a 22 week delivery date; in plastics they cost $33,000 with a 7 week delivery date.

In automotive tooling, duplicate models are usually required by various production departments. For example, tooling departments require as many as three duplicate master models of a given auto body panel: one for constructing dies, one for constructing assembly fixtures, and the third for constructing inspection fixtures. Such exact duplicates can be made much more rapidly in plastic than they can in plaster or wood.

The light weight of plastics (laminates are about 1/4 the weight of steel, a little more than 1/2 the weight of aluminum; cast resins are about 1/7 the weight of steel, a little less than 1/2 the weight of aluminum) is often of particular benefit for this type of tooling. Duplicate models and dies, and prototype and display parts must often be transported or shipped to other installations. Reducing weight reduces transportation costs. Reducing weight of production and inspection tools that must be handled frequently provides direct benefits in faster manual handling of tools and reduction in worker fatigue.

For example, a complete auto body side-assembly checking fixture, 15 ft long and 5 ft wide, weighs over 2200 lb in steel; in plastic it weighs only 642 lb. Another example is a bluing rack used for spotting an auto hood panel die; this weighs 640 lb in a Cerro alloy and 140 lb in plastics.

Ease of repair and revision can be an important benefit, particularly in models, patterns and dies used for design development. Cured material can be removed by sanding, filing or sawing followed by patching where necessary. Where areas must be built up, patching putties or laminated patches can be applied.

Limitations of Plastics

One of the important limitations of plastics for auxiliary tooling lies not so much in the plastics materials themselves, but in their misuse due to lack of understanding of their behavior. For example, one automotive tool engineer points out problems they have had in having to rework production tooling because a production panel did not check out in the inspection fixture. The reason for the error was that the original plastic model used for the die did not check out with the inspection fixture. The plastics tool had warped in storage. Such costly failures obviously raise strong doubts in the tooling man's mind about the utility of plastics.

Plastics tools can be produced with excellent dimensional stability. But such tools cannot be made in a haphazard fashion with the lowest-cost plastics materials. Although auxiliary tools may not be primary load-bearing structures, many of them, such as locating and inspection fixtures are critical tools in that any dimensional inaccuracy will be reflected directly in production parts and assemblies. Consequently, they must be fabricated properly with the proper materials.

There are many possible causes of lack of dimensional stability in a plastics tool. If tooling materials are not formulated, applied and cured properly they may set with internal strains that will result in distortion of the tool in time. Also, when combining plastics and metals in a tool, the design must take into consideration the coefficients of thermal expansion of the two materials. Methods of avoiding possible warpage in such tools are discussed in more detail in Chapter 8.

Three other common causes of inaccuracy, in auxiliary tooling according to Weaver[6] are: (1) distortion in a plaster mold, (2) improperly prepared supporting structure, and (3) surface abrasion.

Since the plastics tool will only be as accurate as the master from which it is made, extreme care must be taken in producing the master. Distortion may result from expansion of plaster masters during setting. Plaster splashes should always be checked back to the pattern or model after setting. In some cases (particularly when masters are to be reused), plastic rather than plaster masters should be made from the original clay, wood, metal or other pattern.

Plastics have relatively low moduli, as compared with metal, and consequently will deflect relatively easily under load. Thus, supporting structures must be sufficient and properly prepared. Welded metal tubing should always be normalized to prevent distortion in the final tool. Other base constructions, whether they consist of plastics tubing, aluminum, Kirksite, iron castings, plaster or board, must be capable of remaining stable under whatever loads, temperature changes, and handling are to be encountered in the shop. As a general rule, the fixture surface should never be expected to carry the base under load.

From the strength standpoint, the stresses which the tool may be expected to undergo both in use and misuse must be evaluated. Of course, tooling cannot be designed for the careless worker, but evaluating the type of production operation for which the tool is designed, and the type of worker who will be using it, can provide a good indication of the type of handling the tool will receive.

Surface abrasion can cause inaccuracies in a tool. Areas of apparent abrasion, such as gage pins and locating blocks, should usually be made of conventional metal tooling materials. Metal edging of areas subject to frequent contact is also advisable. Of course, the addition of metal to fixtures increases both cost and weight. These sacrifices must be balanced against the need for optimum operating efficiency in each particular tooling situation.

Surface abrasion is particularly troublesome in fixtures and gages to be used with metal castings. The normal roughness of as-cast metal surfaces can abrade plastics rapidly. In a fixture of this type, possibly plastics should only be considered a convenient matrix for the location of metal inserts.

Heat resistance of plastics can be a limiting factor in some types of auxiliary tooling, such as welding fixtures and some drill jigs. In welding jigs intermittent exposures to relatively high temperatures can be tolerated, but during exposure, loads must be low. Proper attention, of course, should be paid to dimensional variations to be encountered in such cyclic heating conditions. Also, in such applications plastics have low thermal conductivity, and consequently will retain the intermittently applied heat for a longer time than metals. Re-exposing a plastics to heat too rapidly may cause build-up of heat to the point of degradation.

The heat generated by a revolving drill in drill jig bushings can become excessive, and result in softening or degradation of the material surrounding the bushing. In such cases, either a higher-temperature resin may be used to pot the bushing in the fixture, a ceramic cement may be used, or a bushing may be pressed into a steel plate, which is then bent to the contour of the tool and laminated or cast into the face of the tool. Use of a steel plate permits more even distribution of the heat over the area of the plate, and consequently reduces the concentration of high temperatures in the plastics material around the bushing.

Another approach is the use of replaceable type bushings riveted or screwed to the face of the tool.

Other limitations not commonly encountered would exist where materials chemically react with the tooling plastic and result in tool failure, e.g., delamination of paint masks in a caustic soda bath.

Master Pattern

In the initial design stage of any product, the first three-dimensional concept, or the master pattern, is either (1) an artistic design problem, or (2) a mechanical "lofting" problem of translating a two-dimensional drawing into a three-dimensional form.

In the artistic modeling of a pattern, where "style" is being developed, modeling clay is still the most widely used material. It has the workability required, and remains workable for a relatively long period of time.

In translating a drawing to a three-dimensional pattern, wood is often used, machined to the final dimensions. A relatively new plastic material appears to offer some benefits in replacing wood for such patterns. Several producers have developed low-density epoxy pattern boards. The materials have densities of about 35 to 45 lb/cu ft, with compressive strengths of about 6000 to 8000 psi, tensile strengths of about 1600 psi, flexural modulus of elasticity of about 140,000 psi, and water absorption of about 3 per cent after 2 hr in boiling water.

The materials are reported to have the machinability of wood, but no grain (thus properties are isotropic), and negligible swell or shrink with changes in moisture. They can be drilled, sawed, shaved, planed, nailed, sanded and jointed. The materials are also available in liquid form for casting, or in a workable, clay-like consistency. Figure 11.1 illustrates an interesting new use for the material.

Another method commonly used to "translate" two-dimensional drawings into three-dimensional models or patterns is the loft template method. This involves erecting templates at various "stations" and building up a pattern by the splining technique, between the outer periphery of the templates. Plaster has been the conventional material for such patterns. Thixotropic epoxies are receiving increasing attention for this use. The splining technique using both plaster and plastic is described in Chapter 7.

Reproduction—Materials and Methods

The greatest benefits of plastics are usually obtained after the initial shape is produced, i.e., the ease of reproducing that shape in plastics. This is true in reproducing the initial pattern to provide duplicate models; reproducing the initial die model to provide duplicate die models; reproducing certain areas of a production panel to provide accurate locations for checking or drilling fixtures; and reproducing many other types of auxiliary tooling.

In selecting the material and method best suited for reproducing a particular tool, the requirements of that tool must be studied. Actually, all the plastics discussed in Chapters 4 and 5, and all the fabrication techniques discussed in Chapter 7 may be used to provide the best tool. In general, epoxy resins are probably the most widely used material for highly accurate models, duplicates, and auxiliary tooling, since accuracy in the tool usually requires the low shrinkage and excellent dimensional stability of epoxies.

Where the utmost in dimensional accuracy is not critical in a laminated tool, polyesters can provide lower cost, excellent handling and processing characteristics and good structural strength. But their higher shrinkage, and the fact that they set rapidly with much of the shrinkage taking

(*Ren Plastics, Inc.*)

Figure 11.1. New model-making method, developed and patented by Creative Industries, is reported to cut auto surface-development programs from 8-12 months to as little as 13 weeks. Basically, the steps are as follows: 1) A plaster mold is made of one half of a full-size styling clay model, and suitably bulkheaded. 2) After cure, the mold is removed (as shown, top), and set up on a surface plate. 3) The workable clay-like epoxy plastic is then applied with suitable supports to the inside of the plaster model to a thickness of about 1 in. 4) After cure of the plastics, the

place in the "set" condition, makes accuracy extremely difficult to attain, and may result in warpage of tools or "show-through" of reinforcement.

Models and duplicates and auxiliary tools can be produced by mass casting, surface casting, or laminating. Mass or surface casting of either epoxies or phenolics provides minimum-cost tools, as the process is simple and rapid. Mass casting is often used for such tools as prototypes, display models, and duplicate models. Phenolics may be used, but usually require an oven cure, and care must be taken that materials in contact with the liquid mix are not attacked by the acidic-type catalysts used. Care must be taken with epoxies that excessive exotherm is not generated in massive castings. Cast tools, though low in cost, are relatively brittle.

One of the most common requirements for auxiliary tools is an accurate, durable surface contour, such as that required by bluing blocks, drill jigs and cages, contour and trim line checking fixtures, etc. A common fabrication technique is laminating the desired surface with glass cloth or mat-reinforced epoxy, and backing with a tubular supporting structure.

A typical fabrication technique for such a structure is as follows (details of each step are outlined in Chapter 7):

1. Metal or reinforced plastics tubular supporting structure is prefabricated on a level base plate or surface plate.
2. The tooling surface is then laid up on the plaster or plastic master with conventional laminating techniques.
3. Before the final layer of cloth or mat is applied to the laminate, the supporting structure is moved into place. The ends of the tubing or pipe in the supporting structure are butted into the wet laminating resin. The final layer of reinforcement is applied to the back of the laminate, tying in the supporting structure to the laminate.

Joints between supporting structure and the back of the laminate can then be reinforced, if necessary, with glass tape or ribbon impregnated with epoxy resin. Or an epoxy paste or putty can be used to reinforce and fillet the joints. For maximum strength between supporting structure and laminate face, flat plates or pads may be attached to the ends of the

---

plaster mold is removed; modifications or alterations can be easily made, since the material can be worked like wood. 5) Plastic faced metal templates are shot against the body surface and used to make metal templates. 6) The matching half of the model is then made symmetrically with the first (as shown in photo, bottom; part of stacking cube has been removed to better show the construction). 7) After cure, individual panels can be fenced off, female plastics impressions taken from them, and male laminated die models (the desired end product) molded against the females.

tubing structure at the point of attachment to the laminate. Such pads provide maximum strength joints, bonding well with the wet resin on the back of the laminate. These joining techniques are shown in Figures 7.8 and 7.9 in Chapter 7.

(*Shell Chemical Corp.*)

Figure 11.2. Supporting structure for fixtures is shown by this welded steel pipe structure for a master gauge used for the entire nose of Lockheed's Hercules C-130. The back of the epoxy laminated tool surface can be seen through the supporting structure. The tubular frame was pushed against the back of the laminates just after the last layer of resin was applied, providing sufficient adhesion between frame and tool surface.

Another common technique is to surface-cast a thin layer of resin to form the actual pads or working surfaces of the tool. After the supporting structure is fabricated, cloth- or mat-reinforced epoxy laminates are laid up to the approximate desired shape on the attach areas of the supporting structure. A model or prototype of the part for which the tool is to be used is first treated with a parting agent and blocked into position so that each laminated pad on the supporting structure is about $\frac{1}{8}$ to $\frac{1}{4}$ in. away from the surface of the model. Epoxy resin is then cast between the pads and the prototype or model, accurately reproducing the contour of the part in the area of each pad.

As can be seen, any of a wide variety of fabricating techniques can be used for fabricating these types of tools. The specific technique will depend on the tool engineer's understanding of plastics and their fabricability.

The following specific case histories will indicate both the materials and construction versatility available, and the benefits obtainable. The

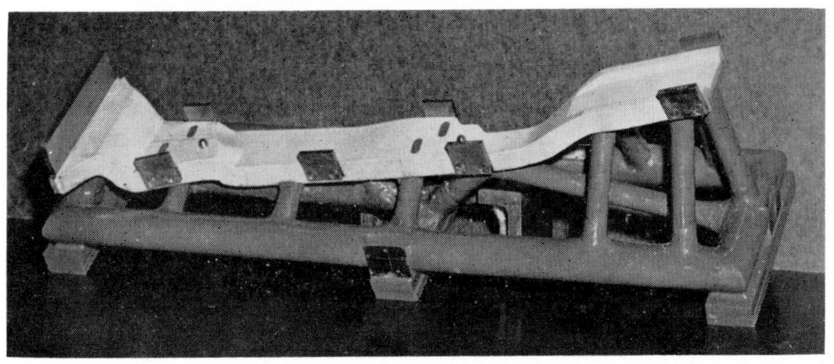

(*Rezolin, Inc.*)

Figure 11.3. Typical of the most widely used construction for auxiliary tooling is this fixture for checking auto center pillars. Tool surface is laminated (or may be surface cast) with a tubular supporting structure.

specific tools given below are limited to somewhat unusual tools, since a great deal has been written and reported on the more conventional tools.

Vacuum Chucks. Use of plastics vacuum chucks for milling and machining irregularly shaped castings or forgings can eliminate a substantial amount of machine set-up time and positioning of the part with height gages. The machine operator need only drop the part on the chuck, and by drawing a vacuum, accurately position the part for machining. A typical chuck is shown in Figure 11.4.

Plastics vacuum chucks can be made by either casting or laminating techniques. In casting a chuck, a metal weldment of roughly the desired shape is prepared with suitable holes for vacuum lines. The weldment is positioned over a suitably prepared pattern of the reverse side of the part to be machined (or over the back of the actual part). Epoxy casting resin is poured between the weldment and the mold, or reverse of the part. Vacuum holes to the surface can either be drilled after the resin has set, or pins can be inserted in the weldment prior to casting the surface.

To produce a laminate surface, the working surface of the chuck is laid up on a pattern or a production part, and usually an egg-crate supporting structure filled with an aggregate-resin mix is built up on the reverse side of the laminate.

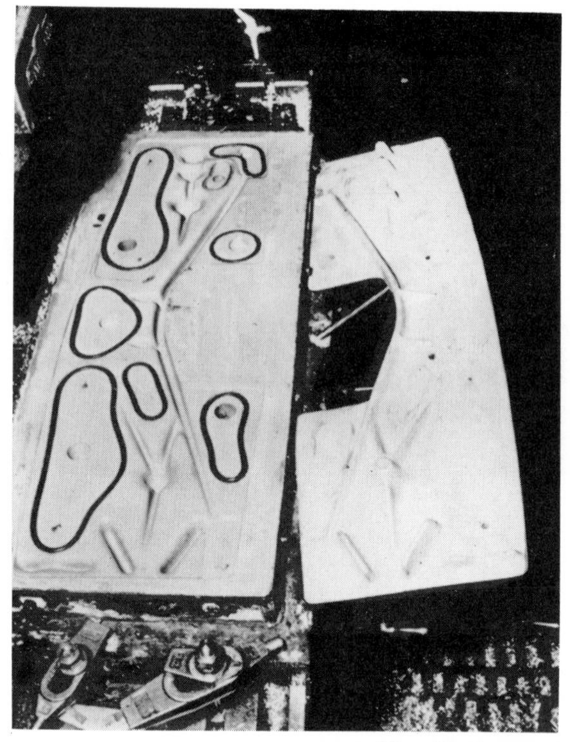

(*Ren Plastics, Inc.*)

Figure 11.4. Cast epoxy vacuum chuck, shown at left on milling machine, provides rapid, simplified locating of parts to be milled.

Paint Spray Masks. Plastics paint spray masks do not tear and distort as paper may do, yet they are more resilient than metal in fitting closely to a coutoured surface. The problem is to produce a mask to suit the specific requirements, hitting the proper compromise between durability and weight.

Convair, for example, found that paper templates were occasionally torn by the air pressure used in spray guns. Cleaning up was costly and time-consuming. A mask made of glass-reinforced epoxy behaved satisfactorily, but weighed 35 lb and was considered too heavy.

Their solution, described by Fullarton,[3] was to use a ¼-in. thick honeycomb material. Two layers of glass cloth and resin were applied to each side of the honeycomb to form the faces of the sandwich structure, and the edges were built up with 1-in. wide glass tape and epoxy to a thickness of $\frac{3}{16}$ in. to provide close fitting masking edges. The mask performed well, yet weighed only 20 lb.

(*Shell Chemical Corp.*)

Figure 11.5. Reinforced epoxy paint spray masks made by Resin Fabricators and used by Outboard Marine Corp. of Canada to paint their two tone motors. Fabrication is described in the text.

The solution to the problem of two-tone painting of production outboard motor shrouds for Outboard Marine Corp. of Canada, is described by Martin [5] of Resin Fabricators. The shrouds are aluminum die castings, which are polished smooth prior to painting. The hand-polishing and finishing of the metal causes small dimensional differences from shroud to shroud. Because of these differences rigid metal masks would not fit all shrouds accurately. With the 40 psi spraying pressures, any small gap between mask and shroud resulted in fuzzy paint lines.

The problem was solved by laminating a resilient glass-epoxy laminate for the main structure of the mask. The edges of the mask, which are the only point of contact between mask and shroud, are made of a flexibilized epoxy resin. The edges of the mask hold the main laminate out $\frac{1}{8}$ in. from the shroud surface. The resilience of the edging material is sufficient to absorb variations in shroud dimensions, yet is rigid enough to be clamped firmly to the shroud.

In fabricating the masks, a sample shroud is first coated with $\frac{1}{8}$ in. of pattern maker's wax to form the laminate $\frac{1}{8}$ in. from the shroud surface. Holes and strips are cut in the wax to allow for the $\frac{3}{8}$-in. wide resilient edge and for certain locating points. The shroud areas are treated with a silicone mold release agent, and one half of the edge areas and location points are filled with a resilient epoxy paste material, flush with the top of the wax. Precut glass cloth is then laid over the whole area and saturated with epoxy laminating resin. The number of layers of cloth used depends on the size of the structure. During lay-up, metal clamping devices used in production to hold the masks to the shrouds, are molded into the laminate.

After the resin gels firmly at room temperature, the mask is removed, the wax stripped and ragged edges of the laminate trimmed. The mask is then replaced on the shroud and oven-cured at 150°F, for the particular system used. After curing, the final half of the $\frac{3}{8}$-in. edge is made by applying the paste material, and curing at room temperature.

When masks are not in use, they are stored in-place on the shrouds to preclude any possible distortion. In production, masks are cleaned of paint build-up every seventh use by soaking for several minutes in toluol and brushing.

Surface Plates and Tables. One of the many special uses of plastics in auxiliary tooling is in fabricating surface plates. One technique, described by Fullarton,[3] is first to weld up and sandblast a steel table. The table is placed upside down on a suitably prepared surface plate with $\frac{3}{8}$-in. spacers between the plate and the inverted table top. A casting epoxy is then poured to fill the space. Such tables have the same degree of smoothness as the original surface plate, and are inexpensive, lightweight and corrosion-resistant.

This technique can also be used for producing small work tables used for beating out and repairing sheet metal detail parts. Larger tables can be made by setting up two or more surface tables, aligning them with optical instruments and filling the cracks between them with plaster or putty before casting the surface against the tops.

Electrical Discharge Electrodes. Electrodes for electrical discharge machining, such as the Elox process, have been produced by metal-spraying a plastic mold. For acurate surfaces, a plaster mold should be sprayed, then the metal surface backed with cast resin. For such applications, the bond between metal and plastic does not have to be extremely strong. Such electrodes have been produced by Dix Engineering.

Coil Winding Forms. Coil winding forms made of cast epoxy resin are reproduced with substantial cost reduction by the Small A-C Motor Department of General Electric. The forms are cast in RTV silicone rubber molds, and bonded to a wooden base. Used in pairs, original hard wood forms cost $86 a pair when ordered in quantities of 25 or more pairs. As

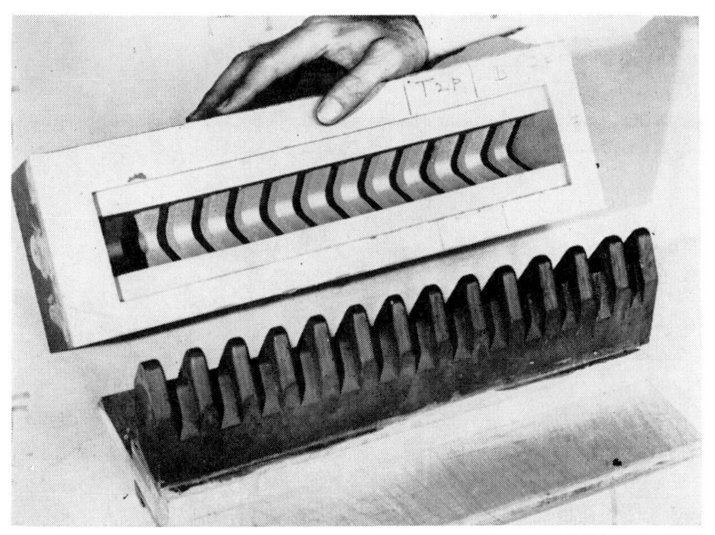

(*General Electric Co.*)

Figure 11.6. Epoxy coil winding forms cast in RTV silicone rubber mold are much cheaper than wooden forms. They are described in the text.

epoxy castings, the forms cost only $16 per pair. Also, delivery time was reduced from 3 weeks to 2 days, and service life of the forms has been increased.

Assembly Fixtures. An assembly fixture designed by the Appliance Motor Department of General Electric is used to assemble motor switch components on an automatic machine. Originally machined from laminated plastic, the fixtures required jig-bored holes for locating pins which had to be held to center-distance tolerances of ± 0.002 in. The fixtures cost $175 each when ordered in minimum quantities of 60.

The fixtures are now cast with epoxy resin in an RTV silicone rubber mold, complete with pin inserts, at a cost of $10 each.

REFERENCES

1. Delmonte, J., "Low-Density Epoxy Pattern Boards," paper presented at 15th Annual Conference, Reinforced Plastics Div., The Society of The Plastics Industry, Inc., Feb. 1960.
2. Dutt, D. E., "Simplified and More Accurate Model Reproduction with RTV Silicone Rubber," paper presented at Annual Meeting, American Society of Tool Engineers, Apr. 1959.
3. Fullarton, A. M., "Practical Plastic Tooling Ideas," *The Tool Engineer* (Oct. 1959).
4. Griffith, R. E., "Now Gages are Made of Plastics," *American Machinist* (Aug. 27, 1956).
5. Martin, C. B., "Reinforced Epoxy Spray Masks For Two-Tone Painting," *Plastics Technology* (Jan. 1958).
6. Weaver, W., "Known Limitations of Plastic Tooling," paper presented at the 25th Anniversary Meeting, American Society of Tool Engineers, Mar. 1957.

12. *Plastics-Forming Tools*

Plastics-forming tools are those molds or dies used to form either thermosetting or thermoplastic materials. They may consist of plastics surfaces which directly form the plastics materials, or they may consist of plastics materials backing metal surfaces which directly form the plastics materials.

Plastics molds have been relatively widely used and are well accepted for short-run contact or vacuum-bag molding of reinforced plastics and gravity-feed casting of thermosetting resins. (Actually, the fabrication of a laminated or cast plastics tool in plastics master molds or patterns is an example of plastics tools being used for plastics forming.)

Plastics molds are also being used for vacuum-forming thermoplastic sheet; some success has been had with matched plastics molds for preform-molding of glass fiber-reinforced polyester resin. Some experimental work has been carried out in developing matched plastics molds for compression molding of thermosetting molding compounds, and for injection molding of thermoplastics. But if a potential exists in plastics for compression and injection molds it is far from being realized.

Primary Advantages

The benefits of plastics tools for plastics forming are the same as those for plastics metal-forming tools. Namely, lower tooling costs, shorter lead time, lighter weight tools, and ease of repair and revision. Reducing costs permits more rapid amortization of tooling and shorter economical production runs, i.e., one manufacturer defines limited production as somewhere between 500 and 1000 parts.

Limitations

The thermal characteristics of plastics materials represent the largest single problem in the use of plastics tools for plastics forming. Their low heat resistance is a drawback; even more important is their poor heat-transfer characteristic.

Most plastics-forming processes require heat and usually pressure, either during the forming operation or to cure the material. And the mold material must either distribute the heat uniformly and rapidly over the mold surface to all areas of the plastics part being formed, or it must rapidly dissipate forming heat to cool the part. The low thermal conductivity, even of filled tooling plastics, concentrates heat in localized areas of the mold. Depending on the forming process and the material being formed, this can result in (1) unsatisfactory parts, (2) long, uneconomical molding cycles, and/or (3) distortion of the mold. Some types of molding processes, e.g., compression and injection molding, require the combination of high temperatures and pressures, a combination not suitable for best performance of plastics.

New Materials Developments

The more recent materials developments of primary interest for plastics-forming molds include: (1) resin and reinforcement systems with improved strength at higher temperatures: e.g., pressure-cast high-temperature epoxy resins reinforced with metal fibers, and RTV silicone rubber molds which permit oven-cure of cast epoxy resins; (2) techniques for providing plastics molds with metal surfaces which have excellent thermal conductivity, as well as good strength and abrasion resistance: e.g., gas plating and electroless nickel plating; and (3) development of resin, filler, and reinforcement systems with substantially improved thermal conductivity, as well as improved heat resistance.

Characteristics of materials and processes in items (1) and (2) above have been discussed before in some detail: pressure-cast high-temperature epoxy resins in Chapter 4, RTV silicone rubber in Chapter 5, and plating techniques in Chapter 6. Following is information developed recently on improvements in thermal conductivity obtained by various resin, filler and reinforcement combinations, reported by O'Connor and White.[2]

In the work reported, test molds were fabricated by (1) slurry casting, (2) spraying, and (3) pressure casting of copper or aluminum fiber reinforced materials and aluminum powder filled materials.

In evaluating heat resistance, a 100 per cent epoxy resin with an anhydride high-temperature cure was used as a control. It lost 18.2 per cent weight after 4 days at 440°F. A composition containing 80 per cent aluminum powder in a high-temperature epoxy resin ("Devcon" C) lost

9.5 per cent weight after the same exposure. Although some specimens of aluminum powder-filled material, to which about 20 to 32 per cent metal fibers had been added, lost as little as 6.3 per cent weight after the same exposure, O'Connor and White conclude that the addition of metal fibers in itself does not substantially affect weight loss on exposure to heat.

On the other hand, fiber reinforcement substantially increases thermal conductivity. Low fiber content provides conductivity comparable to high filler loading. Compared with a conductivity of 0.080 Btu/hr/sq ft/°F/ft for the unfilled epoxy control, conductivity of slurry-cast 80 per cent aluminum powder filled resin was 0.34; conductivity of spray molded fiber and resin (fiber content ranging from 23 to 28 per cent) ranged from 0.25 to 0.30 Btu/hr/sq ft/°F/ft.

Of the molds made by slurry casting, the highest conductivity (0.91 Btu/hr/sq ft/°F/ft) was obtained using a combination of 32 per cent fiber and 68 per cent powder-resin system; of those made by spray molding, the highest conductivity (0.74) was obtained using 17 per cent fibers in the aluminum powder filled-resin.

Of all the systems and fabricating techniques evaluated, the highest thermal conductivity was obtained in pressure-cast molds, cast and gelled at 300 psi pressure. This should be expected since pressure casting permits use of higher fiber content and denser packing of the fibers. Such molds containing only 55 per cent fiber reinforcement showed conductivity of 5.6 Btu/hr/sq ft/°F/ft; thermal conductivity was increased to 11.93 by using a combination of 38 per cent fiber and 62 per cent powder-resin base. Weight loss of these two compositions after 4 days at 440°F was 5.9 and 7.2 per cent respectively.

These techniques do appear promising for improving epoxy molds for plastics forming. However, compared with the highest conductivity obtained, i.e., 11.9 Btu/hr/sq ft/°F/ft, conductivities of metals used for molds is about 21 to 27 Btu/hr/sq ft/°F/ft for low-alloy and carbon steels, and 70 to 90 for cast aluminum alloys.

The following sections briefly describe the relative success of plastics tooling in the various plastics-forming processes. Included are molding conditions under which tools must perform, and types of materials and fabricating techniques most widely used or under investigation.

Low-Pressure Laminating

Plastics molds are widely used for molding of reinforced plastics parts by low-pressure laminating techniques, such as contact, vacuum or pressure-bag molding, and by spray molding. Pressures are low, ranging from none for contact to about 10 to 15 psi for vacuum-bag, and up to 50 psi for pressure-bag molding. Both polyesters and epoxies can be cured at room temperature, and even when an oven-cure is desired, typical temperatures and cycles are only about 2 to 5 min. at 220 to 275°F for polyester; 1 to 2 hr at 175 to 240°F for epoxies, followed by a postcure of 2 hr at about 300°F, if desired.

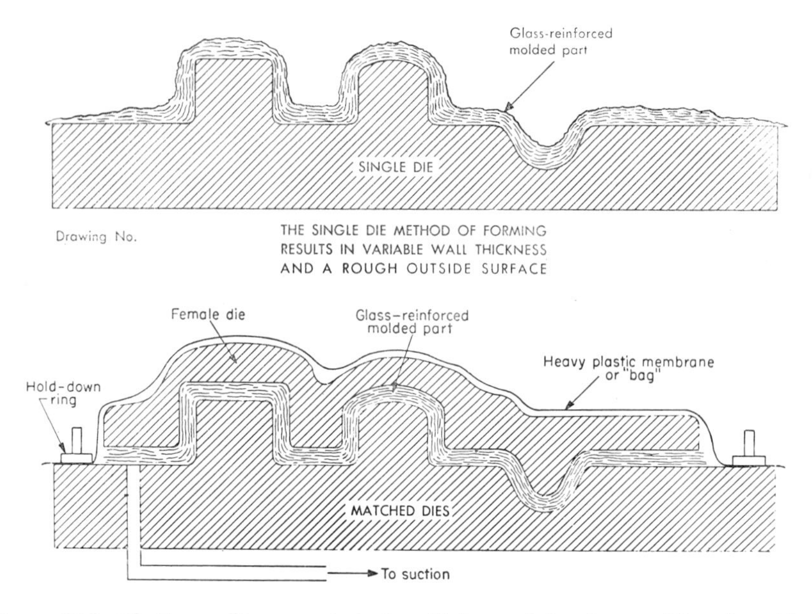

Figure 12.1. Plastics molds are relatively widely used for bag molding by either the single or matched-die method. (*Ren Plastics, Inc.*)

Since most tool engineers interested in molds for reinforced plastics are working in the materials to begin with, they should be well acquainted with both the materials and molding methods. They are well equipped to use both the basic fabricating techniques and specialized methods. Consequently, the following summary is very brief.

Plastics mold materials for low-pressure reinforced plastics may be either epoxy or polyester, depending on the requirements. High-temperature epoxies are used where elevated-temperature cures are applied. Polyesters provide lower cost, excellent handling characteristics and more rapid cure, but they have a higher degree of shrinkage, and where the danger of mold warpage is to be minimized, epoxies should be used. Polyesters are often used for molding polyesters; epoxies for molding epoxies.

If large molds are required, construction usually consists of glass-cloth-laminate surfaces with appropriate supporting structures. A metallic filled gel coat will aid somewhat in distributing heat over the face of the mold. For smaller parts lower cost cast epoxy or phenolic molds can be used.

In vacuum-bag molding, either a single or matched mold may be used. With single molds, the part is laid up on the plastics mold, the polyvinyl alcohol film is laid over it, and the vacuum is drawn. Parts produced in this manner have only one finished side (i.e., the side in contact with the mold). With matched molds, the part is laid up over the male, or inside the female, the second mold member is applied, and the polyvinyl alcohol film encloses both members, the vacuum pressing the two molds together to form a part with two finished sides, as shown in Figure 12.1.

Water-Soluble Mandrels for Reinforced Plastics

A promising new development (early 1960) is a family of hot-melt, water-soluble thermoplastic mandrel materials for use in filament winding, fabrication of reinforced plastic ducts, or other shapes with complex interiors where mandrel removal may be a problem. It should replace plaster in many applications. (It is also reported to be an excellent material to stabilize honeycomb for machining.)

The material (called "Paraplast" by its developer, Rezolin Inc.) is available in several grades, differing essentially in color and pouring temperature (ranging from 310 to 330°F for the lowest temperature material to 520 to 550°F for the highest), and differing somewhat in strength (compressive strengths range from about 17,000 psi for the lowest temperature grade to 19,000 psi for the highest). Coefficient of linear thermal expansion is about $3.8\text{-}4.1 \times 10^{-5}$. Cost ranges from 37 to 59¢/lb, depending on quantity.

The grade of compound selected will depend to a degree on the temperature and time of cure required for the plastics part which is to be formed over the mandrel. For example, the low-temperature melting grade has a maximum heat resistance of about 275°F; the highest-temperature melting grade has heat resistance of about 475°F.

Molds for forming the mandrels should have uniform wall thickness if possible, and may be of aluminum or laminated high-temperature epoxy. Laminated molds should usually be bag-molded and postcured to obtain maximum heat resistance.

According to Rezolin, the mandrel material should be melted (in any of a variety of types of melting equipment) and the mold stabilized at a specified temperature (e.g., for grades with pouring temperatures of

heat evenly over the mold surface, and then in cooling the formed part, it is beneficial in some cases in eliminating chill marks on the formed sheet due to cooling the mold too rapidly.

Pressures generated by vacuum forming would not appear to be high, but vacuum over an area of 30 x 50 in., for example, exerts a total force of about 10 tons.

(*Marblette Corp.*)

Figure 12.3. Sheet has been vacuum formed over a gang of 12 epoxy molds.

In general, only the higher temperature resins are used in making molds. Although phenolics were initially used, improvements in heat resistance of epoxies have caused them to replace phenolics in many cases. One of the most common fabricating techniques is the use of cast, filled epoxies, reinforced at points of high stress with fibrous glass roving, cloth or mat. The use of metal fiber-reinforced epoxies appears highly promising. Surfaces may be sprayed and flocked and cores may be pressure cast.

Cooling the mold to increase cycle time may be accomplished by embedment of copper tubing for water cooling, or by use of metal mesh to increase thermal dissipation.

Cast Mold Surface. Typical of the casting method of mold making is the technique used by Chanal Plastics to fabricate water-cooled molds. A plaster female is splash-cast from the master pattern. To provide a smooth finish on the mold, a sheet of PVC (polyvinyl chloride) is vacuum-formed into the female plaster.

The interior of the PVC draw is then reinforced with a plaster splash, and a wooden frame or mold box is built around the inverted PVC draw. The PVC is treated with appropriate mold release agents, and prepared pins are inserted against the PVC wherever air holes are required in the mold for the vacuum-forming process. At this point, copper tubing is installed within the frame to provide water cooling.

The epoxy casting resin is then mixed and poured into the frame. The depth of pour permissible at one time will depend on the formulation and the peak exotherms anticipated. The material is allowed to gel, and the mold is oven-cured to obtain maximum heat resistance.

After curing, the plaster splash is broken away from the mold, and the PVC draw and the vent hole pins are removed. The model is placed on the bed of the vacuum-forming machine and the ends of the copper tubing are attached to the main water line.

Chanal has used such molds in gangs of 12 to a bed for thermoforming polyestyrene planters. Cycle times of 60 sec are common with the water-cooling system. Water cooling is relatively expensive, but Chanal has found that though not economical for very short production runs, on longer runs the shorter cycle pays for the system.

Metal Fiber-Reinforced Mold Surface. The use of metal (primarily aluminum) fiber reinforcement in the mold surface provides substantial improvements in mold heating and cooling. As indicated before, thermal conductivity can be further improved by combining the metal fiber reinforcement with an aluminum powder-filled material.

A typical method of producing such a mold is as follows: First apply a 1/32-in. coat of an aluminum powder filled gel coat. Then spray or flock aluminum fibers on the wet resin. The resulting coating is allowed to cure for about 30 min., depending on the resin, or until slightly tacky. Aluminum fiber and resin are then sprayed on the back of this surface coat to build up a ¼-in. thickness. At intervals during spraying, the material should be compacted with a spatula or roller to remove air bubbles and densify the fiber mat. Provisions for vacuum holes can be made either prior to spraying by inserting prepared pins in the mold, or by drilling after the coating is cured. The mold may then be cured overnight at room temperature, removed from the pattern or master mold and postcured. (A typical postcuring cycle might be 2 hr at 210°F, followed by 4 hr at 250°F.)

The base or core for the mold may be of wood or metal, depending on the requirements of the vacuum-formed part and the machine. Highly successful results have been reported with pressure-cast metal fiber-reinforced epoxy cores. According to Mazzucchelli,[4] a 22 x 24-in. mold made

(*Smooth On Mfg. Co.*)

Figure 12.4. Vinyl wading pool formed by Chanal Plastics, indicates the size of epoxy vacuum forming molds feasible. The mold weighs over 300 lb and uses an aluminum-filled epoxy resin and a special hardener to minimize exotherm.

by pressure-casting steel fiber-reinforced high-temperature epoxy has produced over 2000 signs in acrylic (polymethyl methacrylate) and cellulose acetate butyrate sheet. At last reports the mold was still running with no difficulty.

In an evaluation test, Union Carbide Plastics compared molds made by pressure-casting aluminum fiber-filled high-temperature epoxy, with molds made of solid cast epoxy systems filled with silica, aluminum powder and aluminum shot, and a cast aluminum mold. Molds were used for vacuum forming a food container of 0.050-in. impact polystyrene. Although the pressure-cast mold did not perform as well as the cast aluminum mold, it was reported to produce satisfactory parts at higher operating temperatures than any of the epoxy molds, indicating that faster cycles would be possible under comparable conditions.

Metal-Surfaced Plastic Molds. Molds consisting of a metal surface backed with plastic provide (1) intricate surface detail, (2) good thermal conductivity and good control over heating and cooling of the mold, and (3) longer mold life. Production runs with such a mold may be as high as a million pieces, but they are seldom used for deep draws. They are usually used for shallow molds such as are used to produce place mats, bath mats, etc.

To date, most metal-surfaced molds are produced by spray metallizing with zinc and aluminum. The coating is sprayed on a master mold to a thickness of $1/16$ to $1/4$ in. The master mold may be of plaster, plastics or other material. Prior to spraying, pins for vacuum holes are inserted in the mold. After the desired metal thickness is built up, cooling coils can be incorporated, and bonded to the back of the metal surface by spraying around them. The metal coat is then backed with cast epoxy resin, and after cure the pins for the vacuum holes are removed.

Unfortunately, sprayed metal coatings are relatively brittle, and cannot stand abuse without destroying surface detail. Butzko [1] estimates the cost of such molds at $75 to $100/sq ft.

The newer techniques of gas plating and electroless nickel plating appear highly promising for producing high-production molds. As yet, the economic and technological problems have not been completely solved.

An important problem in metal-surfaced molds can be the differences in thermal expansion coefficients which exist between the metal surface and the plastics backing. Using zinc or aluminum surfaces, the problem is not too severe, as zinc has coefficients of about $13\text{-}18 \times 10^{-6}/°F$, and aluminum has coefficients of about $12\text{-}13 \times 10^{-6}/°F$. Cast, unfilled epoxies have coefficients ranging from $17\text{-}50 \times 10^{-6}/°F$, but a variety of filled epoxies are available with coefficients ranging roughly from 14 to $25 \times 10^{-6}/°F$. In using nickel plates the problem becomes greater, as nickel has a coefficient of about 8 to $9 \times 10^{-6}/°F$.

Differences in expansivities of surface and backing materials are particularly important in applications such as vacuum-forming molds, in which heating and cooling is cyclic.

Matched Die Molding

The use of matched plastic molds for molding reinforced plastics has been limited, primarily due to the need for even and rapid distribution of heat over the mold surfaces (to obtain efficient cycles), and the higher pressures used in the process. Pressures may range from about 100 psi to as high as 400 psi.

The bulk of the work in plastics molds for such moldings has been for molds used to form reinforced polyester resins. Mold temperatures of 220 to 250°F are common, depending on the size and shape of the part.

One of the important benefits plastics molds would offer in this process is in economically getting into production quickly. Actually, matched die molding of reinforced plastics is often used for high-production quantities of parts which can be produced by slower low-pressure lay-up techniques. Since it is a relatively high-production process, the use of plastics molds could (1) provide temporary tooling while waiting for metal molds to be fabricated, or (2) provide the economies inherent in the process for shorter production runs because of lower tooling costs.

Although a variety of constructions have been worked with, one of the most promising appears to be the pressure-casting method. Such tools may incorporate metal pinch trims and inserts where required.

Mazzucchelli [4] reports a matched-mold pressure-casting of aluminum fiber-filled high-temperature epoxy, which was used to produce over 730 vending machine panels. The panels were glass reinforced-polyester, 0.060 in. thick. The two halves of the mold were about 75 x 44 in. and each weighed about 600 lb. They varied in thickness from 3 to 4⅜ inches. A hardened steel pinch trim in the form of 9 x ½ x ⅜ in. deep strips were screwed into the male and female mold members with sufficient clearance between them to allow for expansion.

The mold with an aluminum fiber content of 46 per cent was pressure cast with 300 psi pressure. Shrinkage of the mold varied from 0.0006 to 0.001 in./in., with the lower shrinkage occurring across the irregularly shaped areas.

Although an initial problem of scum build-up in the mold was encountered, it was minimized by baking a silicone coating on the mold surface.

The mold was built in 4 weeks and sold for $5950, compared with an estimated cost of $9000 to $12,000 for a cast, machined aluminum mold and $15,000 to $25,000 for a machined steel mold.

The use of metal-surfaced plastics molds appears promising in reducing mold surface problems. With the sprayed metal surface, porosity appears to be a problem in picking up resin and thus reducing surface quality as well as hindering release of parts from the mold. The newer gas and electroless plating promises to eliminate these problems.

Molds for Casting Plastics

Casting of plastics materials may involve (1) mixing a liquid thermosetting resin with suitable catalysts or hardening agents and pouring into a mold where it is cured either with or without heat; (2) melting a thermoplastic resin and pouring it hot into a mold where it hardens on

(*General Electric Co.*)

Figure 12.5. Accuracy obtainable in RTV silicone rubber molds is shown by this 0.030 in. thick cast epoxy actuator ring. No parting agent is required.

cooling; or (3) pouring a liquid thermoplastic material into a mold and fusing by heat.

In all of these techniques, plastics materials have been used as molds, the determining factor (economic considerations aside) being either the chemical compatibility of ingredients in the mix with plastics materials used for molds, or heat to which the mold will be exposed, caused by either curing or fusion temperatures required. The emphasis here is on newer developments in plastics mold materials.

One of the most interesting new developments is the use of RTV (room-temperature vulcanizing) silicone rubber as a flexible mold material for casting epoxy resins. Unfortunately, little work has been done investigating the compatibility of the RTV silicone with other types of casting resin systems.

Extremely fine detail on the mold is achieved only by eliminating any air pockets or imperfections on the pattern surface. A convenient technique for achieving this is by surface-coating the master pattern with RTV silicone prior to pouring the mold. The surface preparation is done by carefully painting RTV silicone over the entire surface with a small brush. Since RTV silicone requires no parting agent, this surface preparation does not actually add to the over-all mold production expense. Also, the addition of a silicone fluid to the RTV silicone lowers viscosity and aids in reproducing sharp surface detail. Also, painting the surface of the mold with epoxy resin prior to casting will insure accuracy of surface detail and remove any surface bubbles.

Where intricate surface contours must be reproduced and castings must be completely bubble free, pressure-casting techniques can be used. After casting the epoxy in the RTV mold, the filled mold is put into an autoclave (a paint-spray pressure tank can be used), and put under 50 to 80 psi pressure. The pressure should be maintained until the epoxy has entirely cured. According to Dutt of General Electric removal of the mold before the epoxy has entirely cured may result in poor surfaces on the part.

Life of an RTV mold is primarily dependent on the types of resin systems cast. For example, strong amine hardeners will substantially shorten the mold life, i.e., possibly only about 6 or 8 parts can be produced. Suppliers of RTV silicone rubber (General Electric Co. and Dow Corning Corp.) should be consulted to determine the material's reactivity with specific chemicals used in the casting resin system.

Injection, Compression and Transfer Molding

Injection molding of thermoplastics requires pressures on the order of 10,000 to 25,000 psi on the molding material, with about 25 to 75 per cent of these pressures being transferred to the mold itself. The material in the heating cylinder is maintained at temperatures on the order of 300 to 600°F. The mold is usually cooled to permit solidification of the charge when it hits the mold. As can be seen, these are severe requirements to be met by a plastics mold material.

Compression and transfer molding of the thermosetting plastics involves pressures on the order of 2000 to 10,000 psi at mold temperatures of 300 to 350°F, or whatever temperature is required to cure the material being molded. Again, these are severe requirements for a plastics mold material.

Because of these high pressures and temperatures and the requirements for thermal control over the mold material, little success has been encountered in the development of plastics molds. Also, these processes are primarily used for volume production, where actual tool cost is amortized over a large volume of parts, consequently interest has not been too high in developing plastics molds. However, such molds if developed to commercial satisfaction could substantially reduce the volume of parts required to justify the use of the process.

The most promising developments appear (again) to be the metal fiber-reinforced pressure-casting technique, and the use of gas or electroless nickel plating techniques to provide metal mold surfaces.

According to Weaver, Modern Pattern and Plastics has made successful compression and injection molds for prototype production. They have been successful in molding on the order of 50 to 100 parts. Weaver points out that the answer appears to be the use of gas-plated coatings of steel or iron, backed with high-temperature epoxy reinforced with metal fibers. Molds may be electrically heated by calrods, or by steam in copper tubing embedded in the mold.

REFERENCES

1. Butzko, R. L., "Plastic Sheet Forming," New York, Reinhold Publishing Corp., 1958.
2. O'Connor, R. T., and White, J. J., "Heat Conductivity Epoxy Formulation for Low Cost Molds," paper presented before 16th Annual National Technical Conference, Society of Plastics Engineers, Jan. 1960.
3. Massie, U. W., "Fin Tip," *Aircraft and Missiles Manufacturing* (Oct. 1958); "Epoxy Resin Molds in Vacuum Forming," *Product Design and Engineering* (June 1959).
4. Mazzucchelli, A. P., "New Fiber-Reinforced Epoxy Compositions," paper presented before the Society of The Plastics Industry, Inc., Reinforced Plastics Div., 13th Annual Conference, Feb. 1958.

13. *Plastics Tools in the Foundry*

The use of thermoplastic materials as patterns for investment casting probably represents one of the earliest uses of plastics as a tooling material. But the acceptance of plastics for other types of foundry tooling has been more recent than in other industries. Reluctance on the part of foundrymen has probably been due primarily to the need for durable tools. Foundry tools must often withstand rough treatment, and sand is highly abrasive.

The first plastics used for foundry tools were the phenolics, which are relatively hard and brittle, with poor abrasion resistance. (Phenolic resins, of course, are used as binders for sand in the shell mold-casting process. However, since in this process sand is actually the mold material, with phenolic resin serving only as the binder, such molds cannot be considered plastic molds.) Some work has been done with ethyl cellulose where improved resilience and abrasion resistance were required. Now, with the degree of resilience obtainable in epoxy resins, plastics tooling has become well established in the foundry.

Foundry tools made of plastics include patterns and core boxes, core prints, blown core boxes, core driers, and duplicates of these tools. Plastics are also being used for repair and salvage of metal tools, for filling blow holes in ferrous and nonferrous castings, and for many other uses.

Pros and Cons

Primary benefits for foundry tools include (1) low cost of duplication, (2) light weight, in comparison with metal patterns, (3) ease of release from sand molds, (4) ease of alteration and repair, and (5) reduction in tool fabrication time.

Any adequately equipped pattern shop can produce plastics tools with no substantial new expenditures beyond materials costs. Also, the plastics materials can be used for repair and revision of both metal foundry tools and finished castings, in some cases. The excellent parting qualities of plastics from sand often provides the additional bonus of improved quality of castings.

The limitations of plastics in the foundry are essentially those outlined in Chapter 11 for models, patterns and prototypes. But the rough treatment which can be expected in a foundry puts a premium on durability of the tool.

Where plastics are considered for a tool, the type of service to which the tool will be subjected, as well as the type of handling to be expected should be carefully evaluated.

Materials and Methods

Cast phenolics can be used for some types of patterns, but dimensional fidelity is not that obtainable in epoxies. Also, phenolics are more brittle, and less resistant to abrasion.

Epoxy resins are now probably the most widely used plastic for foundry tools. Where a degree of resilience or impact strength is required, flexibilized types are common. For small tools, such as small patterns, match plates and core prints, the simplest and most economical method is casting. For larger tools, surfaces can be cast and backed with a suitable core of cast phenolic or epoxy resin, cast aggregate or other types of supporting structures. Or for large tools, where maximum dimensional stability and strength are required, tool surfaces may be laminated and backed with a suitable supporting structure.

The following descriptions of fabrication techniques indicate typical methods of making different tools. After becoming well acquainted with plastic materials, and the fabrication techniques outlined in Chapter 7, specialized techniques can be developed to solve specific foundry tool problems.

Casting Tools. For small tools, wood or plaster masters are mounted on a suitable board and prepared with parting compound. Epoxy casting resin, usually flexibilized with either polysulfide (Thiokol) or polyamide (Versamid) resins, is merely mixed and poured. Wooden lightener cores can be used to reduce both weight and cost.

For larger tools where cores are desired, surface-casting techniques are used. The mold or master cavity is lined with 1/4 to 1/2 in. of wax or sheet "Celastic," and a parting agent is applied. An epoxy or phenolic core resin, filled with pea gravel or other type of low-cost aggregate (where machinability is desirable crushed walnut shell in epoxy is used), is mixed and poured. After cure, the core is removed and the wax or

Celastic removed. The core is then suspended in its previous position, and epoxy surface-casting resin is mixed and poured between core and mold.

For pouring core boxes, the core print is mounted on a flat board, and a wood frame is set around the print to the dimensions of the core box. All surfaces are prepared with parting compound. If necessary, the box can be reinforced with a lightweight steel frame.

Marblette suggests placing a ¼-in. thick layer of felt inside the mold and covering it with a sheet of polyethylene. A core resin is poured, filled as described above. After cure, the core is removed, and the polyethylene and felt discarded. The core is suspended in the original position, and the resin is cast between the core and mold.

Epoxy resins filled with either steel or aluminum powder can also be used. They are available in liquid or paste form. Types with approximately 80 per cent metal powder filler provide surfaces with pseudometallic qualities. Such materials are also widely used for patch and repair of both plastic and metal tools.

The casting techniques, where applicable, usually result in the lowest cost tools. For example, according to Devcon Corp., a pattern cast with a metal powder-filled epoxy can require only 16 hr as compared with 38 hr for a corresponding pattern in wood. Costs of both material and labor for such a typical pattern are quoted as being $56 in plastics, versus $118 in wood. Of course, time and costs will vary widely according to the specific tool.

Laminated Tools. One of the common laminating techniques for producing a master mold and duplicate patterns is shown in the 9 steps in Figure 13.1, and described by Kish.[3]

The first step is to build a plastics mold for the pattern. The original wood or plaster pattern is mounted in a drag, and the seams and joints are caulked (step 1). After preparation of the drag and pattern with parting agents, an epoxy laminating formulation mixed with hardener is brushed over the pattern and drag. After the surface coat has started to set, another coat is brushed on. Then layers of glass cloth are applied; these may be either preimpregnated or impregnated with epoxy resin in the mold. Usually, a thickness of about $3/16$ in. is built up by successive plies (step 2).

An epoxy core resin is then prepared and poured against the back of the laminate, covering the highest part of the pattern to a minimum depth of 1 in. (step 3). The mold is then cured, usually for about 24 hr, depending on the resin system used. After cure, the drag is inverted and the wooden board and original pattern removed. The finished plastic mold (step 4) can now be used to make any number of duplicate patterns.

To make patterns from the plastics mold, the latter is polished and proper parting agents applied. Caulking compound is then applied over the entire mold surface to a thickness of about ¼ in. (step 5). The purpose of the caulking compound is to provide a space to be filled with

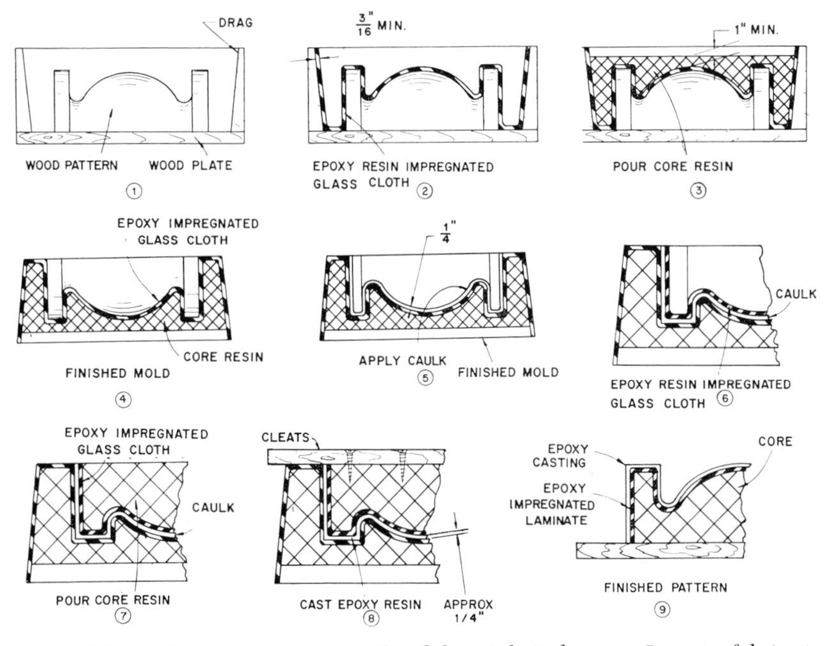

Figure 13.1. Typical procedure as outlined by Kish Industries, Inc., in fabricating molds and duplicate patterns for the foundry. Steps are detailed in the text. (*Shell Chemical Corp.*)

surface-casting resin; consequently other materials, such as sheet wax, etc., can also be used.

A few small holes are then dug in the caulking at various points on the mold surface. These holes will be filled with epoxy resin to form locating pins and will help space the pattern from the mold to permit casting the surface coat. The caulking compound is then treated with parting agent. An epoxy resin surface layer is applied (or at least sufficient resin should be permitted on the surface to fill the holes in the caulking compound), and glass cloth-epoxy laminations are applied to a thickness of about $\frac{3}{16}$ in (step 6). After the laminate cures, epoxy core resin is mixed, poured, and allowed to cure as before (step 7).

Cleats are then screwed into the back of the partly finished pattern, and the pattern is removed from the mold. The mold is cleaned of all caulking compound, and fresh parting agent is applied to the plastic mold. The laminate surface of the unfinished pattern is then sanded to provide a good bonding surface, and is replaced in the mold, appropriate space between pattern and mold being maintained by both the cleats and the locating pins cast to the laminate surface. The space is then filled with an epoxy surface-casting resin formulation, to slightly above the level of the mold (step 8). After about a 12-hr cure, the finished pattern is removed. Surface imperfections can be repaired quickly with an epoxy patching putty.

Specific Techniques

A variety of techniques are actually used in producing different foundry tools. Differences exist primarily in the type of backing or supporting structures used. The following specific procedures are typical:

Large Pattern. Johnston [2] outlines techniques used to fabricate a large plastic pattern, 38 x 48 x 6 in. thick. The pattern is subjected to the severe jolting action of a 10,000 lb jolting machine. After mold preparation and application of a gel coat, 14 layers of glass cloth-epoxy resin are applied. The laminate is then backed with $\frac{3}{4}$-in. thick aluminum ribs cut roughly to the shape of the back of the laminate. Aluminum cross ribs are added to provide an egg-crate core. In addition to adding support, the aluminum structure provides a good mounting surface for the tool. The aluminum structure is drilled and bolted securely to a pattern plate.

If interchangeable, or if core "locating" prints are to be added to the pattern, steel inserts are used. Such inserts must be large enough to provide a good bond with the resin, and should be rough-ground, which both aids mechanical bonding, and eliminates all oil and grease from the surface.

The inserts can be installed prior to laying up the laminate; they can be installed midway in the laminating operation; or they can be installed by grinding out suitable areas after the laminate is cured, and bonding with a resin paste, or resin filled with chopped glass or roving. In any of these methods, there must be sufficient plastic and glass cloth contact area to firmly hold the insert.

Core Box. Johnston also points out several methods of producing laminated core boxes. Instead of making a wooden core box as the initial step, a core plug or dummy master is made to the exact inside shape of the core box. At this point the procedure differs depending on whether a steel facing will be required on the face of the core box. Such a facing is generally used on production core boxes to minimize wear on the strike-off surface. When a steel core box surface becomes worn, the steel facing may be easily replaced with a new steel surface, bringing the core box back to the proper dimension. On the other hand, without the steel face, the plastics face may become worn sooner, but such a face is

(*Devcon Corp.*)

Figure 13.2. Steel-filled epoxy resin is cast by Alloy Steel Casting Co. in plaster mold to form half of a loose pattern. Wooden strips are lightener cores which become part of the finished pattern. Finished duplicate patterns are shown on next page.

Figure 13.2. (*cont'd*) Finished duplicate patterns shown with mold.

easier and more economical to repair. The decision depends on the economies of the specific situation.

If a steel facing is desired, three methods can be used to apply it:

1. Steel is cut to match the shape of the core plug, and is filed to fit tightly around the base of the core plug. After attaching the core plug to a flat mounting plate, the steel facing is doweled in place on the mounting plate, and the core box is laminated over and around it.
2. The second technique involves installation of steel after the core box is fabricated. The core box is laminated against the core plug which has been attached to mounting plate. Additional laminate thickness should be built up in the flange area where the steel facing is to be located. After stripping the cured laminate, a suitable groove for the steel facing in the flange area is machined, and the facing inserted, bonding with resin.
3. The third method, and the one Johnston prefers, is to machine the core plug (or the face that will eventually become the face of the core box) an amount equal to the thickness of steel facing to be used. The foreshortened core plug is then attached to the mounting plate and serves

as the mold for the laminated core box. After cure, the box is stripped from the plug, and steel facing is added to the full width of the flange. The steel facing is then filed or otherwise machined to match the contour of the core box.

Whether steel facing is used or not, the core box is laminated on the core plug to the desired thickness. After sufficient thickness is built up, a metal supporting structure should be added to the back of the core box for additional strength.

Although various structures can be used, Johnston describes a satisfactory structure consisting of aluminum strips built up to form an egg-crate structure. The structure is then bonded to the laminate with laminations of glass cloth-epoxy resin, with additional strips of resin-saturated cloth or tape extending over the cross-members and laminated into the back of the box. Fillets and additional support for the junction of egg crate and core box can be provided by epoxy putty or paste.

Ingot Mold Pattern and Core Box. Fabrication of an ingot mold pattern and core box at a cost reduction of more than 30 per cent is described by Grimes.[1]

A dummy master is fastened to a straight, level surface board. A parting agent is applied to assure release of the plastic from the dummy, and two layers of epoxy surface coat are brushed over the entire surface of the dummy. The surface layer is built up to a $\frac{1}{16}$-in. thickness. When the surface coat becomes tacky, two layers of glass cloth are laminated with epoxy resin and pressed well down into the second surface coat.

An aluminum skeleton or framework (in the form of an egg-crate type structure) is then set into the last layer of glass and epoxy resin while the resin is still tacky. This provides the structural support. Additional layers of cloth and resin are then applied until a shell thickness of $\frac{1}{4}$ to $\frac{3}{8}$ in. is built up. The core-box half thus produced is allowed to cure for 24 to 36 hr before removal of the surface board. After the surface board is removed, the dummy is left in place and the other half of the dummy is doweled to it. This insures a perfect match of the two halves of the core box.

The ingot mold pattern is built up in a similar manner. A core print is formed in the wooden mold with two layers of epoxy surface coat and two layers of glass cloth to a thickness of $\frac{1}{8}$ inch. Additional thickness to the surface of the wooden mold is then built up with crushed walnut shell-filled epoxy casting resin.

The ingot mold pattern is a cylinder about 8 in. in diameter and 33 in. long. It is built up in two halves in the wooden mold using glass cloth-reinforced epoxy resin and an aluminum skeleton supporting structure. After the two halves are cured, the joint areas are faced on a disk sander and bonded with epoxy. The solid core print is then fastened to one end and a ½ in. aluminum plate is bolted to the top.

The above examples of laminated constructions indicate the difficulty in pinpointing costs of such tools. Estimates vary. Johnston [2] mentions that a laminated-plastic pattern may cost as little as one-third that of a good aluminum machined pattern. Since the bulk of the costs are labor, Johnston's itemized estimate of time required to fabricate a laminated pattern may be helpful:

1. Preparing and pouring plaster mold—3 hr.
2. Preparing completed mold with plastic sealer and release agents—3 hr.
3. Surface coating and laminating the pattern—5 hr.
4. Setting up completed mold on milling machine and machining raw edges of plastics pattern—4 hr.
5. Removing laminated pattern from mold, and making any necessary repairs to surface (if required)—2 hr.
6. Replacing production pattern with new pattern—3 hr.

Total time—20 hr.

Modification and Repair

The ease of repair of plastics tools can be of great benefit in foundry tools. The basic techniques are those described in Chapter 8.

The excellent adhesion of epoxy resins to metals can be put to use in modifying and repairing metal foundry tools at substantial cost savings. For example, Grimes [1] describes the salvaging of a 30-in. aluminum valve pattern which originally cost $6000. The pattern would no longer produce a salable casting. The pattern was refaced with glass-reinforced epoxy resin, producing a pattern with better sand release than the original at a cost of $1500, representing a saving of $4500 to the customer.

Johnston [2] reports the economical salvage of a 41 x 48 x 4-in. deep cast-iron core box that had been in production for 20 years. Because of its size and weight, the core box was hand-filed and scraped to size. The box was used to provide one-half of a full core; the other half core was made from this same box, and was reversed and pasted to the first half core. Complete matching of pasted surfaces was considered impossible. Consequently, core makers spent considerable time rubbing the cores to match. This took time, and also meant that excess metal was given away with each casting.

To solve this problem, the core box was washed out to remove all traces of core oil, then shot-blasted to expose the cast iron. Epoxy was brush-coated on with glass cloth to areas in excess of 1/32 in. in thickness. The core box was then machined with a light-duty milling machine, since only plastic and some light cuts of cast iron had to be removed. Areas were thus faired in, with feather edges in spots, and the core box was salvaged, reducing production cost of the core by 25 per cent and eliminating give-away metal with each casting.

Specialty Applications in the Foundry

The number and types of specialty applications for plastics as foundry tools are dependent on the engineer's knowledge of plastic materials, and his imagination in putting them to work.

An excellent example of this is the process announced in early 1960, making use of foamed polystyrene in a modification of the "lost wax" process for casting metal sculpture. The technique called "foam vaporization" was developed by A. M. Duca through the cooperation of H. Taylor, both of Massachusetts Institute of Technology. The process resulted from Duca's efforts to reduce the cost of casting sculpture by the lost-wax technique.

As used for sculpture, the lost-wax process involves making an undersized model, coating it with wax and modeling the details of the sculpture in the wax. The finished wax is then coated with plaster, the wax is melted out, and metal is poured into the cavity left by the removal of the wax.

The new foam vaporization process is much simpler. The statue is carved from a block of polystyrene foam, using simple woodworking tools. The completed carving is enclosed in a sodium silicate sand mold. (When carbon dioxide is pumped through the packed mold, it reacts with the sodium silicate, "reinforcing" the sand.) Then the metal is merely poured into the mold. The heat of the molten metal vaporizes the polystyrene foam, and as the mold fills the vapors are driven off.

Benefits of the process, according to Duca, include (1) reproduction has extremely high fidelity because the shape of the first model is reproduced directly in metal, (2) foam polystyrene is readily available and no more expensive than wood, (3) it is lightweight (densities range from 1.8 to 6 lb/cu ft), eliminating supporting structures such as those commonly required in large clay models, (4) the process can be carried out in existing foundry facilities, and (5) because reproduction is direct, the artist does not have to rely so heavily on various types of craftsmen to reproduce his detail.

(*Massachusetts Institute of Technology*)

Figure 13.3. Model carved in polystyrene foam to be cast by the new "foam vaporization" process, described in the text. Sand will be packed around this 30 in. Pegasus, carved by A. Duca, and when the metal is poured into the mold the polystyrene foam will vaporize, permitting the molten metal to fill the sand mold, reproducing the foam model with high fidelity.

Although this technique is a dramatic example of plastics in the foundry, others are less so but may be more widely applicable. For example, several investment casting foundries have experimented with epoxy dies to replace soft metal dies for wax-pattern injection. In one experimental case, such substitution resulted in a reduction in die cost from $2000 for the soft metal die to $200 for the epoxy die. The lower thermal conductivity of the plastic resulted in longer cycles. However, possibly the newer pressure-casting technique using metal fiber reinforcement in high-temperature epoxy may provide more practical dies.

REFERENCES

1. Grimes, R. E., "Plastic Patterns and Core Boxes," *Foundry* (Oct. 1958).
2. Johnston, T. S., "The Application of Reinforced Plastics for the Foundry and Pattern Industry," paper presented at 15th Annual Conference, Reinforced Plastics Div., The Society of The Plastics Industry, Inc., Feb. 1960.
3. Kish, S. P., "Duplicate Patterns with Epoxy Resins," *The Tool Engineer* (Jan. 1956).
4. "Plastics in The Foundry Industry," Technical Bulletin, Marblette Corp.

14. *Miscellaneous Tools and Future Development*

There are many miscellaneous applications of plastics for tools. Some of the more important are covered in the following sections.

Integral Molds

Integral molds are those molds which actually become a part of the final assembly. Although somewhat different from the accepted concept of "plastics tooling," some mention should be made of them. The technique is primarily being used in the electronics industry to encapsulate electronic assemblies.

One of the most widely used techniques involves the use of the relatively new epoxy molding compounds. These are of particular benefit because of the extensive use of epoxy resins for potting and encapsulating. Thus, the encapsulating material is made of the same material as the mold.

The epoxy compound is molded by high-production compression or transfer-molding techniques in the shape of a component case suitable to enclose the assembly. The electrical assembly is inserted in the case, and potting or encapsulating resin is poured to fill the case and enclose the assembly. Such operations can be carried out on a rapid assembly-line basis. After cure of the encapsulating material the assembly is complete.

Obvious benefits result from elimination of mold preparation, and stripping of the potted assembly from the mold. Also, the integral mold provides a strong case around the complete assembly.

Nylon Mandrels

Nylon mandrels made from stock shapes are used to help bend aluminum extrusions by Lite Vent Industries, Inc. They are used both as mandrels to fit inside the extrusions and maintain original cross section during machine-bending, and as protective shoes to fit over prefinished aluminum extrusions which must be hand-bent in the field.

The mandrels are used to bend three tubes at a time in a machine. Aluminum tubes are slipped over the mandrels (supplied by National Polymer Corp.) and clamped to the machine table. An air cylinder draws

(*Plastronic Engineering Co.*)

Figure 14.1. Integral molds make use of molded epoxy component case (left), into which is placed an electronic assembly, such as the diode assembly shown in center. After potting, the mold becomes integral with the potting material (right).

the forming roller and the mandrels around the bending plate. Mandrels slide smoothly, without galling, along the rough interior of the tubing. Nylon provides sufficient flexibility to conform to the bend, yet high enough compressive strength to keep the aluminum extrusion from crushing or buckling at the point of bend.

Several types of mandrels are used. Cut grooves or slots, spaced about ½ in. apart along the length of the nylon rod increase flexibility. Longitudinal grooves are cut in mandrels for clearance of internal flash in welded tubing.

For hand bending, nylon shoes are placed over the straight end of an aluminum extrusion. As the forming roller is pulled across the face of the bending plate, the shoe pivots on the plate. The shoe does not mar the finished face of the extrusion.

Stress Analysis Models

A major problem in the application of stress analysis techniques using three-dimensional photoelasticity for complex configurations such as valves has been the difficulty in casting stress-free models. Most such models have had to be machined or fabricated.

However, the Walworth Co. successfully uses epoxy resins cured with phthalic anhydride for such models. They can be cast to any size or shape, and can be cemented together to simulate welded prototypes. Reasonably stress-free cast models can be produced with these resins. Such models are used at Walworth to apply the three-dimensional analysis technique to shapes such as lubricated plug valves and gate valves. In general, the technique is as follows:

The resin model is first heated to a specific temperature (the material's critical temperature); it is then stressed and while under stress, is slowly cooled to room temperature.

When the load is removed, strains are locked or "frozen" into the model. Slices taken from the model at certain important points, such as planes of symmetry or known principal planes, are then examined in polarized light and the stresses computed.

Other Uses

A variety of other specialized applications for plastics have been found in tooling. The building industry is using glass-reinforced polyester for forms and molds for pouring concrete. Benefits claimed include ease of producing complex contours, reduction in cost and weight, and better surface.

Another interesting application is the use of PVC (polyvinyl chloride) as an inexpensive mold for duplicating expensive carved stonework in concrete. The vinyl plastic in liquid form is cast against the suitably prepared carved stonework, and is fused with heat, duplicating exactly the configurations of the stonework.

The vinyl is then stripped from the stonework, backed with suitable supporting structures and used as a mold to pour concrete. A relatively thin grout can be used on the surface to reproduce the details of the mold.

Future Developments

The two areas of most interest for future developments in plastics tooling appear to be (1) metal-fiber reinforcements, and (2) coating or plating techniques for providing a metal-surfaced plastics tool.

As should be obvious from the amount of attention given to metal-fiber reinforcement and the pressure-casting technique in previous chapters, tools made with these materials and by these techniques are highly successful, even at present. Improvements in the future will probably result from developments in the field of fiber metallurgy, e.g., improved fibers and more versatile metal fiber textiles, and improvements in processing techniques. Also, substantial improvements can be made by growing experience in how best to make use of metal fibers available, e.g., applying proper fibers in the proper proportion to tool areas of high wear, and determining optimum metal fiber-resin ratios to provide specific tool behavior.

The development of suitable top-quality metal-surfaced molds is still for the most part developmental, but much work is being done in this area. Essentially, the ideal is to perfect a commercial technique whereby the metal can be deposited on a master mold with fidelity and ease approaching that obtainable with liquid resins. In such cases, of course, the metal provides the desired mechanical and thermal surface characteristics, while the resin provides a low-cost rapid method of providing structural support to the tool.

As mentioned before, the two techniques most promising at present are gas plating and electroless nickel (Kanigen) plating. Although neither process is new, the use of either for tool surfaces is developmental.

Beyond these two areas of development, the biggest single problem to be solved in plastics tooling is the "materials information" problem. There are over 20 basic families of plastic materials, each of which has a number of different members. As indicated by some of the specialty applications mentioned briefly earlier in this chapter, many of these plastics can be put to use to solve tooling problems.

In addition, new plastics are continually being developed and the older ones are continually being improved. Keeping up with developments in the field is a tremendous job. It is particularly difficult when one considers that plastics should not be considered alone as a tooling material to solve all tooling problems.

For an effective large tooling program somewhere within a tooling department, there must be an engineer, or a group of engineers, capable of evaluating objectively plastics, plaster, wood, ceramics, and ferrous and nonferrous metals in the light of specific tooling requirements. He or they must be able to keep informed of all the developments in the materials engineering field in order to select the tooling material that will provide the optimum tool, both from the standpoint of performance and cost.

REFERENCES

1. "Fabrication Problem Solved with Nylon Forming Tools," *Steel* (Oct. 5, 1959).
2. "Materials Selector Issue," *Materials in Design Engineering* (1959-60).
3. Riley, M. W., "Engineers' Guide to Plastics," *Materials in Design Engineering* (Feb. 1959).
4. Riley, M. W., "Impact Thermoplastics: Which One to Use," *Materials in Design Engineering* (Nov. 1959).
5. Riley, M. W., "The New Epoxy Molding Compounds," *Materials in Design Engineering* (June 1959).

INDEX